THE UNIVERSAL TANK

Frontispiece Entering service with the British Army before El Alamein, the Sherman had become the dominant Allied tank in Italy by 1943. The standard version, armed with a dual-purpose 75-mm gun, was used by armoured divisions and tank brigades in the Italian campaign, where this one was photographed in company with British infantry near Florence in August 1944.

Front cover A Sherman Firefly of 4th Armoured Brigade, 2nd New Zealand Division in Italy. Extra-wide grousers have been added to the tracks to improve flotation on soft ground; panels of armour have been welded to the hull front, and the 17-pounder gun has been painted to disguise its length. While not truly 'universal', the Sherman was undoubtedly the most versatile tank in the Western Allies' arsenal and, with this British modification to its main armament, the most effective.

Back cover A Sherman Firefly, with its turret reversed and the rump of its deep-wading equipment still in place, moves inland from the Normandy beaches to play its part in the final drive across Europe, to victory.

THE UNIVERSAL TANK

BRITISH ARMOUR IN THE SECOND WORLD WAR
PART 2

David Fletcher

London   HMSO

© Crown copyright 1993
Applications for reproduction should be made to HMSO

ISBN 0 11 290534 X

British Library Cataloguing in Publication Data

A CIP catalogue record for this book is available from
the British Library

Printed in the UK for HMSO
Dd 0294474 C35 10/93

HMSO publications are available from:

HMSO Publications Centre
(Mail, fax and telephone orders only)
PO Box 276, London, SW8 5DT
Telephone orders 071-873 9090
General enquiries 071-873 0011
(queuing system in operation for both numbers)
Fax orders 071-873 8200

HMSO Bookshops
49 High Holborn, London, WC1V 6HB
(counter service only)
071-873 0011   Fax 071-873 8200
258 Broad Street, Birmingham, B1 2HE
021-643 3740   Fax 021-643 6510
33 Wine Street, Bristol, BS1 2BQ
0272-264306   Fax 0272-294515
9-21 Princess Street, Manchester, M60 8AS
061-834 7201   Fax 061-833 0634
16 Arthur Street, Belfast, BT1 4GD
0232-238451   Fax 0232-235401
71 Lothian Road, Edinburgh, EH3 9AZ
031-228 4181   Fax 031-229 2734

HMSO's Accredited Agents
(see Yellow Pages)

and through good booksellers

Contents

List of Abbreviations   vi

Introduction   1

1   Tunisia, the Churchill redeemed   3

2   One tank for Italy   17

3   The next generation   33

4   The new enemy   58

5   The American saga   68

6   Consolidation   81

7   Liberation   96

8   Final analysis   111

Index   123

Abbreviations

ACV	Armoured Command Vehicle
AEC	Associated Equipment Company
AFV	Armoured Fighting Vehicle
APC	Armoured Personnel Carrier
APCBC	Armour-piercing capped, ballistic capped
APDS	Armour-piercing discarding sabot
APHE	Armour-piercing high-explosive
AVRE	Armoured Vehicle Royal Engineers
BRC&W	Birmingham Railway Carriage and Wagon Company
CDL	Canal Defence Light
CIRD	Canadian Indestructible Roller Device
COXE	Combined Operations Experimental Establishment
DD	Duplex Drive
DTD	Department of Tank Design
FVPE	Fighting Vehicle Proving Establishment
GMC	General Motors Corporation
GS	General Staff
IGS	Imperial General Staff
LCT	Tank Landing Craft
LRC	Light Reconnaissance Car
MLC	Mechanised Landing Craft
OAC	Obstacle Assault Centre
RAC	Royal Armoured Corps
RAF	Royal Air Force
RE	Royal Engineers
RTR	Royal Tank Regiment
TOG	The Old Gang

Introduction

When *The Great Tank Scandal: British Armour in the Second World War, Part 1* appeared in 1989, I was not prepared for the response. From every quarter, and from all walks of life, I heard from people whose experience, either in industry or the firing line, coincided with what I had written about the poor standard of British tank development in the early war years. In many letters and conversations my conclusions were supported and amplified. I took this as a particular compliment, because these were people – dozens of them – who had first-hand experience of what I had written about, which is a lot more than I have had. There were complaints, too. I was accused of being too flippant, of selecting evidence to suit my conclusions and of denigrating people who had only been doing their best. This is not unfair comment, but it was by no means typical: the most common reproach was from people who wanted to know how much longer they would have to wait for *Scandal*, Part 2. Unconscionably long, I'm afraid, but here it is.

The Great Tank Scandal covered the period from the outbreak of war in 1939, roughly to the winter of 1942/43, when the Allies made their victorious entry into Tripoli. It was a tale of triumph over adversity, but of adversity which was not entirely of the enemy's doing. Drawing on the extensive resources of the Tank Museum library, I was able to uncover a very sorry story of political, industrial and military ineptitude that condemned British and Commonwealth soldiers 'to fight on ponies against an enemy mounted on fullsize horses', as one senior officer put it. The facts thus revealed fully justified the title, which was borrowed from a *Picture Post* article published shortly after the war. *The Universal Tank: British Armour in the Second World War, Part 2*, carries the story forward to 1945. The title was chosen in this case to represent an ideal which recurs throughout the book and is, ultimately, almost realised at the end. As the previous volume showed, British tanks were classified by function, which was fine just as long as one had the right type of tank in the right place at the right time. The fighting in the desert soon revealed the fallacy of this policy, but it was not until Bernard Montgomery took command of the Eighth Army that the alternative was articulated. Detached as he was from the world of tanks, Montgomery could at least see that if one tank could be designed which would fulfil most roles it should simplify matters considerably.

The facts will show that Britain failed to profit from this wisdom until it was just too late. The pattern of tank development which had been established in 1939, of complementary classes of light, cruiser and infantry tanks, was already too ingrained to be changed at short notice, and indeed it appeared to get even worse when a new class of assault tank was introduced in 1942. However it was realised in a sense with the widespread adoption, of necessity, of the American Sherman tank by 1943. Although it has never been the intention to compare the Allied tanks with their German counterparts it is, perhaps, worth remarking here on some specific points. By 1942 the British Army was equipped, worldwide, with up to sixteen different models of tank, three of American origin. With but one exception, the Sherman, all suffered to some degree from poor design, outdated construction, thin armour, weak guns or chronic unreliability – and often from combinations of most of these. In that same year the Germans had three basic models in service, of which two – the Panzer III and Panzer IV – were superior in most of the above respects to every Allied tank except the Sherman. However, by the end of the year they had produced the Tiger, which represented a huge leap forward in terms of armour thickness and gun power at the sacrifice of reliability and quantity production. Taking technology by the scruff of the neck, the Germans went on to build even larger and more powerful tanks without ever regaining the edge in reliability, and, with their massive commitments on the Eastern Front, fell so far behind both the United States and the Soviet Union in quantity production that they were doomed to be overwhelmed.

For those who anticipate precise continuity from the previous title, a few words of explanation are necessary. Some subjects – self-propelled guns and the further development of anti-aircraft tanks, for instance – have been dropped. This is not particularly for want of space, but because those subjects are better suited for a separate volume. Space limitations, however, have curtailed the inclusion of general war history even more than in *Scandal*, but at the same time, I have been able to tap a new resource which was not readily available in 1989: a virtually complete set of Royal Armoured Corps Regimental War Diaries for the entire period, which are now held by the Tank Museum library. These have enabled me to get much closer to user opinions and have revealed all manner of things which the technical archives do not cover. This is reflected, to some extent, in a different approach to the organisation of chapters in the book: in all except the last, the main theme of armoured vehicle development and usage predominates, so that the interesting, but technically complex, subject of specialised armour has been

1

treated as a separate topic, in order not to interrupt the basic tale.

With the publication of this book, I have completed a series of titles which chronicle the development of British and Commonwealth armoured vehicles from 1900 to 1945 in five volumes.* At the time of writing, all five are still in print; in view of current publishing trends I regard this as a remarkable act of faith on the part of my publishers. Thus I wish to pay overdue tribute to Philip Glover and his staff at HMSO for their assistance and confidence. I also wish to thank everyone who has helped me over the years, and for this volume in particular, Ed Bartholomew at the Royal Marines Museum, Brian Baxter at the Royal Electrical and Mechanical Engineers Museum, Colonel John Nowers of the Royal Engineers Institution, Phil Dyer, Ron Huggins and Bart Vanderveen.

*The other four titles, in historical order are:

War Cars: British Armoured Cars in the First World War, HMSO, 1987.
Landships: British Tanks in the First World War, HMSO, 1984 and 1992.
Mechanised Force: British Tanks Between the Wars, HMSO, 1991.
The Great Tank Scandal: British Armour in the Second World War, Part 1, HMSO, 1989.

1 Tunisia, the Churchill redeemed

Shaking off the sand of the Libyan Desert, and with the cheers of the Tripoli victory parade ringing in their ears, in early February 1943 the men and tanks of Eighth Army started to move in Tunisia. Change was in the air; on the ground, the desert landscape was slowly giving way to palm tree plantations and treacherous salt-flats – these, combined with German mines, booby traps and ambushes, made pursuit costly and difficult. For these reasons, it was perhaps fortunate that there was no urgency: until the port facilities in Tripoli could be restored to shorten supply lines, a large-scale advance was out of the question.

With this change in terrain in mind, and before embarking upon a more detailed study of particular armoured fighting vehicles, it is worth remarking on the nature of tank warfare in the desert and some of its lessons. In doing so it is also worth remembering that, apart from the brief and unfortunate experiences in France in 1940, the desert had been the combat debut of many British armoured commanders; what they had learned there would inevitably feed back to British tank designers – at least in theory.

One thing that soon became evident to both sides was that in such open country, where natural cover was almost non-existent, it was virtually impossible to approach the enemy unseen. No matter which point of the compass an attack might come from, there was always ample warning, giving the defenders adequate time to bring their tanks round to the new bearing and meet their attackers face-to-face. Action would begin as soon as one side considered itself to be within range. Thus what really mattered, and what crews were soon clamouring for, was thick frontal armour, even at the expense of protection elsewhere on the tank. For their part, the Germans responded by up-armouring the front of their tanks with extra panels of armour, the plates being fitted by workshop facilities in North Africa on a more or less standardised basis. Inevitably, individual crews embellished these modifications with their own handiwork, usually in the form of extra links of track, but their tanks could take it and the real point to note is the prompt German reaction to the situation. On the British side, as already noted in the first volume of this work,[*] most tanks, particularly the cruisers, were incapable of accepting more armour because of the limitations of their suspensions. In so far as photo-

graphic records are any guide, the use of extra track for protection seems to have been resorted to only rarely by British crews at this time. Commendably, most British tank crews preferred to use whatever additional space or weight capacity that was available to carry extra rounds of ammunition, although their penchant for cluttering their tanks up with portable home comforts became legendary, if not notorious. Whether British tank designers were deaf to advice on these lines from the desert front, or already had enough to think about in trying to achieve modest reliability is uncertain, but it seems safe to say that few, if any lessons from the desert war were absorbed at home. In the event, this was probably just as well. The German designers appear to have been more sensitive to user-opinion, but their tanks were fighting on two fronts where, largely by chance, conditions were much the same. The great tank battles in Russia probably had more in common with desert fighting than warfare in any other part of Europe. Thus, although it was not yet in production, the new German Panther tank was designed with extremely thick frontal armour while remaining relatively thinly protected at the sides and rear. Thus, as one British commentator pointed out, while it would have been formidable in the desert, in close country, such as the Italian theatre where it was first encountered by British troops, it proved vulnerable to flank attacks which were much easier to contrive. The point that this comparison makes is that it is unwise to react too dramatically to local conditions except by making local modications, and even more foolish to design a tank for a particular style of warfare, unless that is all one expects to encounter. However, this is not meant to imply any long-sighted wisdom on the part of Britain's tank designers.

As the landscape changed, so there were organisational changes, too. Since the previous summer forces in the Middle East had come into line with those in Britain on the structure of armoured divisions, reducing their composition to one armoured brigade of three regiments and replacing the other armoured brigade with a lorry-borne infantry brigade. Within the armoured regiments there had also been changes peculiar to the region. They had been reorganised on the basis of two heavy squadrons, equipped with M3 Grant or M4 Sherman tanks, and one light squadron employing M3 Stuart tanks where available, or Crusaders where they were not. This applied to the regiments of 2nd Armoured Brigade (1st Armoured Division), 22nd Armoured Brigade (7th Armoured Division) and the independent 8th Armoured Brigade;

---

[*] D J Fletcher, *The Great Tank Scandal*, HMSO, 1989, p 60.

23rd Armoured Brigade still retained Valentines but for the present was reduced to two regiments, 40th and 50th RTR. New equipment was coming through, but only slowly. Among those recently re-equipped were the 11th Hussars, who spent most of February out of the line trading their old Humber Mark III armoured cars for new Daimlers. Early reports suggested that these were a great disappointment, and there must have been more shaking of desert-wise heads over yet another failure of British industry to produce reliable equipment. In this case, however, it was a matter of unfamiliarity. There was very little wrong with the Daimler armoured car: it was an altogether more sophisticated vehicle than the convention- al Humber – what was needed was better training for drivers and squadron fitters. As it happened, 1943 was planned to be the final year of production for the Daimler, which was due to be replaced by the Coventry, a new model developed jointly by Daimler and Humber. How- ever, the Daimler soon proved so popular that there seemed little point in replacing it and while its future was discussed a bridging order for a further 300 was placed. Then, later in the year, it was agreed to continue Daimler production even after the Coventry came on stream.

The 11th Hussars also received their first Daimler Dingo scout cars at this time and rejoiced in them, but for the fact that they could not get enough. The War Estab- lishment for an armoured regiment called for eighteen of them, but only ten could be spared. They were in demand everywhere, for Royal Horse Artillery regiments, all Royal Signals units, brigade liaison officers and others, but the limit was reached when someone noticed that the War Establishment for newly formed self-propelled artillery regiments included a Dingo as the approved mount for a chaplain! In lieu of scout cars, the 11th Hussars were given more Jeeps, and even raised a separate Jeep scouting troop, which soon managed to get itself into serious trouble.

Another new scout car was the American-built White, of which the 11th Hussars operated four; about the only thing it had in common with the Dingo was four wheels. Although the United States Army had never been en- amoured of armoured cars, they developed a series of scout cars between the wars. Originally these were nothing more than touring cars, with most of the bodywork removed and modest patches of armour placed over the radiator and windscreen. Invariably they carried as many machine-guns as it was possible to fit, but they were not a practical proposition for combat and when the Jeep appeared as a four-wheel drive field car, they were soon eclipsed. In their place came larger vehicles, with four-

1   Daimler Dingo scout cars, a Daimler and Humber armoured car of 2nd Derbyshire Yeomanry, formed up in front of an Avro Anson on a North African airfield.

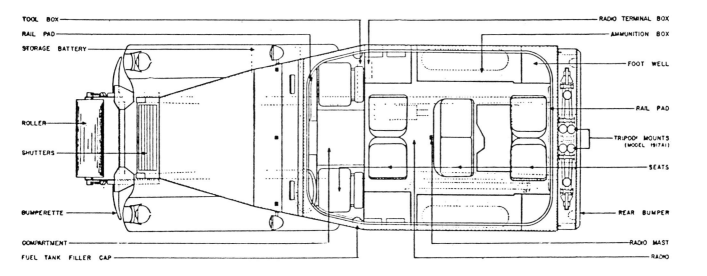

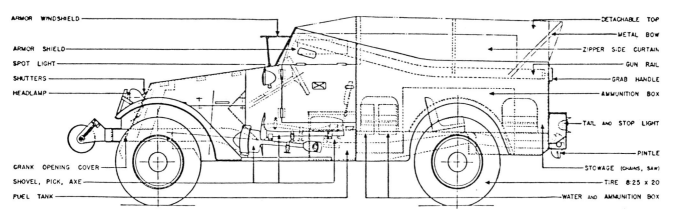

Drawing A: *General arrangement drawings of an M3A1 White Scout Car.*

wheel drive and armoured bodies, which were standardised as the M3 Scout Car in 1938 and the M3A1 in 1940, both of which were more commonly known by their makers' name of White. By British standards they were more like armoured lorries, with a gross laden weight of 5 tons and room inside for up to eight men. Still, the 11th Hussars liked them and used all four in a special scout troop with one Dingo. In addition to a wireless set and one Bren gun, the Whites could carry portable mine-detectors, which were invaluable on the sabotaged roads that led to the Mareth Line. Lacking any armour beneath their chassis, Whites were particularly vulnerable to mines. They were as much in demand as Dingoes, but for different reasons; a report from the Middle East, dated December 1942, described them as most popular. Field squadrons of the Royal Engineers used them, as did the Royal Artillery who still insisted on calling them battery-chargers, while they became fitters' vehicles in armoured regiments, and armoured ambulances, wireless trucks or company recce vehicles with motor battalions. This enthusiasm for the vehicle would no doubt have come as some

surprise to the authorities at home. A White had been tested at Chertsey in July 1941 and the best the report could say about it was that it gave a sound, all-round performance. Protection was said to be more moral than physical – which was true enough, because the body armour was only just over 6 mm thick except in front of the windscreen where it was 12 mm, and even then it was entirely open at the top. However, it was on cross-country driving that the worst problems were encountered. The auxiliary roller fitted to the front bumper, which was supposed to help the car get over obstacles, was described as useless, and even a handicap in some instances. Likewise, excessive overhang of the body behind the rear axle gave rise to grave problems – for a start, it was liable to dig into the ground at any departure from the horizontal, but it was even worse if soft ground was encountered. If the car started to sink in from the back, the first thing that got buried was the rear bumper and with that went the towing hook, so that there was no easy way of getting the vehicle out again. Finally, Chertsey noted, the tyre size on the White was one for which no Runflat type was made.

Experience in the desert was also changing the attitude to armoured cars. This was due in part to the general dilemma over tanks, because the desire was now being expressed for bigger guns. The change in attitude began with the various modifications carried out on Marmon-Herringtons but it was revived with the appearance of the big AEC Mark I armoured cars. These bulky, clumsy machines might well have been dismissed out of hand by cavalrymen of the armoured car regiments, for their high silhouettes and poor mobility since they were hard work to drive and prone to get stuck in soft sand, but instead they proved very popular. Issued at first on the scale of two per regiment, they were used originally to escort echelon transport and protect it from marauding Axis armoured cars. They earned their keep and a good reputation by the power of their big diesel engines which enabled them to pull out other vehicles that got bogged down and they were treated as unofficial recovery vehicles, but they were later welcomed for their firepower and 30 mm thick armour. Towards the end of the desert war the Afrika Korps took to using captured Stuart tanks in their reconnaissance units, which posed a considerable threat to armoured cars. Apart from the AEC Mark I, which was their equal, the only other thing capable of outgunning a Stuart was the ponderous AEC Deacon, a large and ugly armoured lorry mounting a 6-pounder anti-tank gun. They were too unwieldy for the purpose and, while designs were prepared in Britain for a 6-pounder equipped

armoured car, the AEC Mark II, work began in South Africa on a conversion to the Mark I. Known as the Griffin, it used the artillery-pattern 6-pounder in a large but thinly armoured turret. A pilot model was tested by the Mechanisation Experimental Establishment in North Africa, and thirty of the Mark I cars were earmarked for conversion, although there is no evidence to suggest that the scheme was completed. The Griffin should not be confused with the even bigger and uglier AEC armoured car, built on a front-engined Matador chassis at a base

2 *The massive AEC Griffin armoured car at the Mechanisation Experimental Establishment in the Middle East. The hull and its large turret, required to house the 6-pounder gun, are clearly marked Soft Plate.*

3 *The prototype Marmon-Herrington Mark IV which had its 2-pounder gun in a tank-type mounting, seen during firing trials.*

workshops in Egypt. In addition to the Griffin, at least one attempt had been made to officially upgun one of the South Africans' own Marmon-Herrington reconnaissance cars, a Mark III. No precise date is available, nor is it possible to say whether the project originated there or at a British workshop in Egypt. It involved cutting down the hull slightly to the rear of the driver's compartment and fitting a large diameter, open-topped turret mounting a 2-pounder gun and coaxial Browning. This appears to have been a one-off experiment and may have been abandoned in view of the fact that something better was already entering production in South Africa. This was the type which became known as the Marmon-Herrington Mark IV, although its official title, like all the earlier models, was the South African Reconnaissance Car Mark IV, which, in this case, was a good deal less apt. For the first time one could see an armoured car which looked as if it had been designed specially for the job, rather than being an armoured body tailored to, and then dropped upon a conventional chassis. Even so, mechanically the new car was essentially the same, with an 85-hp Ford V8 engine and Marmon-Herrington four-wheel drive components, the difference being that the engine was now mounted at the rear. This resulted in a much better driver's position and greatly improved visibility but the greatest advantage was the provision of a large turret, capable of mounting a 2-pounder gun, all of which meant that the official title of 'reconnaissance car' was a bit of an understatement for a vehicle which physically towered over a British Daimler. Appearances can be deceptive, however: despite its size, the Mark IV was very poorly armoured, with a maximum of 12 mm at the front and no more than 6 mm anywhere else. In particular this affected the turret. When firing trials were carried out using a tank-pattern 2-pounder in a normal mantlet it was discovered that the large turret was not rigid enough to take the shock, so an artillery pattern was substituted, braced to an internal support structure. As with earlier South African models there were differences between those cars built for service with Union forces and those for the Allies in North Africa, but in this case the differences were more fundamental. The first 936 cars were completed in April 1944 at the Dorman Long factory, but in the meantime Britain had placed an order for 1,180 more. Delivery was already in arrears due to supply problems from Britain but the situation was even worse concerning the United States, where the Marmon-Herrington company was quite unable to keep pace with demand. Thus those cars built to the British order used Canadian Ford components instead and were distinguished by the designation Mark IVF. Strangely there is very little evidence of these cars seeing active war service. Possibly they simply arrived too late, or were considered too thinly armoured for their size and firepower; yet there were no complaints about their reliability, and hundreds served for many years after the war, for instance with the Greek Army and Arab Legion.

The designation Mark V was reserved for the huge, Albion engined, eight-wheeler described in the previous volume (*The Great Tank Scandal*, p 98), which turned out to be a notable disaster. The Mark VI was better, but not by that much. It was also an eight-wheeler, although this time with eight-wheel drive from a pair of Ford Mercury V8 engines. These were mounted at the rear, driving through a pair of Ford gearboxes into a transfer box and then to the two Warford driven bogies which had Marmon-Herrington steering axles at their outer ends.

4 *The large, and rather top-heavy looking, Marmon-Herrington Mark VI eight-wheeler. This is the 2-pounder version subsequently sent to Britain for evaluation.*

There were many delays at the design and construction stages, so that ultimately only two prototypes were produced. One, which came to Britain, mounted a 2-pounder gun while the South Africans retained the second example, which carried a 6-pounder. By the time production was ready to begin, the need for such big armoured cars had long gone, but even so there is good reason to believe that the Mark VI would not have been a success. The high profile and narrow track suggest poor stability, while an engineer who tested the car that came to Britain explained that it spent most of its time waiting for new axles to be shipped in because they were always breaking up during trials.

5 *The Marmon-Herrington Mark VII, with its single Vickers machine gun on full elevation, still looks very large for a reconnaissance car.*

6 *The final Marmon-Herrington design to be constructed was the Mark VIII. It had a 2-pounder and coaxial Besa in a Daimler-style mounting, but the turret was open at the top and nearly as long as the body of the car.*

Since they follow in a logical numerical sequence, it is tempting to see the South African reconnaissance cars as representing a continuous line of development, whereas in fact most were contemporaneous designs, at least over a two-year period up to the end of 1943. The Mark VII, for instance, was an improved Mark III which dates from February 1942. It was designed on the Mark III chassis with a low, well-angled body, open at the top where a Vickers machine-gun was mounted. The idea had already been tested in a modified Mark III, but by the time it was ready for production, interest had switched entirely to cars armed with an anti-tank gun and the project was closed down at the prototype stage. The same fate awaited the Mark VIII, which might otherwise have been a most excellent car. The emphasis in this case was on speed and

range, with a sleek, low-line body mounted on a front-engined Canadian Ford F60L chassis. Two versions were proposed; a small arms car mounting twin Vickers machine-guns or a pair of 20-mm weapons, and a 2-pounder car carrying that gun in a very long and low turret, open at the top. A prototype of the 2-pounder car was ready towards the end of 1943, at which point the project was abandoned. By this stage, however, the desire to upgun had spread from tracked to wheeled fighting vehicles and RAC Headquarters in the Middle East told London that they would be happy to have a 17-pounder armoured car if one could be produced, and they were quite anxious to see the new American T18, the eight-wheeled Boarhound, as soon as that could be made available.

In mid-February 1943 the Eighth Army under Montgomery moved up to tackle the Mareth Line, having first defeated a strong but poorly pressed counterattack from three weak Panzer divisions at Medenine. Often known as Rommel's last battle in Africa, it was largely conducted by the Italian General Messe. On 9 March, Rommel, now a sick and weary man, left for good the theatre in which he had made his reputation. The Mareth Line, originally a French defensive system which had been built to keep the Italians out of Tunisia, took advantage of one of the many wadis that fracture the North African coast in this region and which often served as effective tank traps in their own right. Now it was being used by the Italians and Germans to keep French, British and Commonwealth troops out, and a very good job they made of it. Foiled in a head-on assault by minefields, bad ground and a tenacious defence, Montgomery revealed flexible generalship by switching the main thrust of his attack, in the form of 1st Armoured Division, to an outflanking move in the south controlled by General Freyberg's New Zealand Corps. Even this failed to eliminate the Afrika Korps, which now withdrew behind the Wadi Akarit, so that the whole business had to begin again.

At this time, early April 1943, the Axis forces had been in retreat for five months and it would be reasonable to expect morale to have been low. Normally, under these circumstances, shortening supply lines act as a palliative but in Tunisia this was not the case. For one thing the main Axis supply route ran right back to Italy, across a sea and air gap which was increasingly dominated by Allied naval and air forces. For another, by this time large areas of southern Tunisia were in Allied hands following the Torch landings of 7 and 8 November 1942. It would be surprising, therefore, if the men of Afrika Korps had not constantly been looking over their shoulders, even as they stood up to their old adversaries the Eighth Army.

The Torch landings undertaken by General Eisenhower's Allied Expeditionary Force were to be the first major amphibious assault of the Second World War outside of the Pacific, if one overlooks Dieppe, but they were not regarded with undue trepidation. Landings had been

7 *A Humber Light Reconnaissance Car Mark III of 56th Reconnaissance Regiment, looking somewhat the worse for wear. A Boys anti-tank rifle can be seen protruding from the front hull-mounting.*

planned at three locations: one in French Morocco and two in Algiers. The defending Vichy French troops were of doubtful ability and inclination to resist, although in order to avoid provocation everything had been geared to make it appear an exclusively American enterprise and the Stars and Stripes was displayed prominently on all beaches. On the first day, British participation was limited to landing sites either side of Algiers and British armour was represented by one squadron of 56th Reconnaissance Regiment which was destined to form the eyes of 78th Division in subsequent actions.

The vehicles issued to 56th Recce were Humber Light Reconnaissance Cars, developed from the original Ironside model of 1940. Although a Mark II version, carrying a small turret, had been produced in Britain, the main operational model was the Mark III which still employed the Humber Super Snipe chassis, but now with four-wheel drive. The armament included a Bren gun in the turret, on a mounting that allowed it to be used against aircraft, and a Boys anti-tank rifle along with a 4-inch smoke discharger at the front, alongside the driver. Considering that these cars had originally been built as an emergency measure when invasion threatened Britain, it might be surprising that they were still on operational service, invading some-where else, but theirs was not an isolated case. Humbers served in Europe until the end of the war and even in the Far East. If user opinion on these cars was canvassed in 1943 the result is not recorded, but views collected towards the end of the war (the Reconnaissance Corps having been incorporated into the Royal Armoured Corps on 1 January 1944) are equally valid. In its favour crews cited reliability and, no doubt due to the hull shape, a good safety record when mined. They were less com-

plimentary about its high silhouette and particularly its length – it was difficult to turn quickly in an emergency. They considered the armour much too light – it was only 10 mm, against 30 mm on the front of a Daimler Dingo – and it was quite difficult to get out of in a hurry. The Bren gun mounting on the turret was so flimsy that accurate shooting was impossible from a stationary position, never mind on the move, and the location of the smoke dischar-ger meant that it could only be fired in the direction in which the car was pointing – quite useless when one wanted to employ smoke to escape from a dangerous situation. Some Humbers, presumably those of squadron and troop leaders, were equipped as command cars, but they proved too cramped, even if the gunner's seat was taken out. One unit suggested that for this role the turret should be removed altogether, and an extra seat fitted in the back, but there is no evidence to suggest that this was ever done. The Morris Light Reconnaissance Car, a parallel development, also evolved a Mark II version with four-wheel drive and these operated in Tunisia with the RAF Regiment, mounting a similar armament to the Humbers. Both makes were still to be found in service with the British Army after the war in Palestine, but they never really developed from being glorious improvisations with very limited combat value, and were extremely uncomfortable for their crews. If one could say without question that it was simply a shortage of more suitable vehicles that led to their being in service for so long, that might be sufficient justification. Yet the nagging doubt remains that, having once been accepted as just good enough, no real effort was made to replace them because it would be too much trouble and might inconvenience the manufacturers. The Humber was improved slightly into a Mark IIIA version with better vision facilities, but in essence it remained what it always had been, an upmarket motor car with a thinly armoured body.

The first elements of the Royal Armoured Corps to arrive as part of the Torch operation landed on 13 November 1942 through the port of Algiers, not over open beaches. They were B Squadron, 1st Derbyshire Yeo-manry and 17th/21st Lancers which, with supporting arms, were formed as Blade Force. French resistance had already been overcome and it was planned to make a rapid move into Tunisia with the intention of capturing Bizerta and Tunis before the Germans had time to pull themselves together. The Derbyshire Yeomanry operated in Daim-ler scout and armoured cars and Humbers, while the 17th/21st had been issued with a mixture, a very strange mixture, of Valentines and Crusaders. To make matters worse, they also had a full complement of Rotatrailers. The Valentine, with its relatively thin armour and high reliability factor, was issued to armoured divisions in Britain as a cruiser tank for training, but strictly speaking it was an infantry tank and was generally employed as such in Eighth Army. To team it up with the Crusader, which was nearly twice as fast when it was working, seems a strange move, although it was undoubtedly a result of the chronic over-production of obsolete models which had to be used up. There was an element of the hare and tortoise about the affair, although in this version of the fable hare didn't just stop to rest when he was ahead, he had a breakdown.

Since the surviving records are not detailed enough, it is now very difficult to form an accurate picture of the types of Valentine available to the 17th/21st Lancers and other regiments of 6th Armoured Division – 16th/5th Lancers and 2nd Lothian and Border Horse. Photographs can never be regarded as a reliable guide and in any case it is often difficult to identify a Valentine conclusively from a photograph. Those eligible for consideration include Marks II and IV, which had the 2-pounder gun and two-man turrets; Marks III and V, which had the same gun in a three-man turret, and Marks VIII and IX which had the 6-pounder, again in a two-man turret. From a logistical point of view it would make sense that all, in any one regiment at least, should have the same type of engine, either the AEC or GMC diesel, but this is by no means guaranteed. Photographic evidence, for what it is worth, suggests that Marks III/V and VIII/IX predominated in 6th Armoured Division while 23rd Armoured Brigade still had many of the earlier Marks II/IV, and there is every reason to assume that all round, these last two were the most common.

If 23rd Armoured Brigade can be used as any sort of guide, then Marks II/IV would represent the majority, with Marks III/V used as troop and squadron leaders' mounts because the three-man turret made their command duties easier. In 50th RTR at Mareth, reference is made to their having a few 6-pounder Mark IXs, and again this may be typical. In a report to London dated 19 December 1942 Major General Charles Norman, the AFV representative at GHQ Middle East Forces commented 'The 6-pdr Valentine is a bastard, since he [all tanks were of the male gender to General Norman] will have no machine-gun, and his only value will be as a S.P. anti-tank gun with superior armour.' In order to get the 6-pounder into such a small turret while still leaving some room for the crew and a reasonable quantity of ammunition, it was decided to mount it without a coaxial machine-gun. Since the Valentine did not carry a hull machine-gun either, this was regarded as a retrograde step by the troops, most especially in a tank which was supposed to work with infantry, and a local modification was introduced. This involved inserting the barrel end of a .30 Browning machine-gun into a shortened 6-pounder cartridge case with the base bored out. A bracket supported the outer end of the machine-gun on the 6-pounder's recoil guard, which also held an ammunition box, while a remote-control linkage was fitted to the trigger. When necessary, the Browning barrel, enclosed within the cartridge case, was inserted

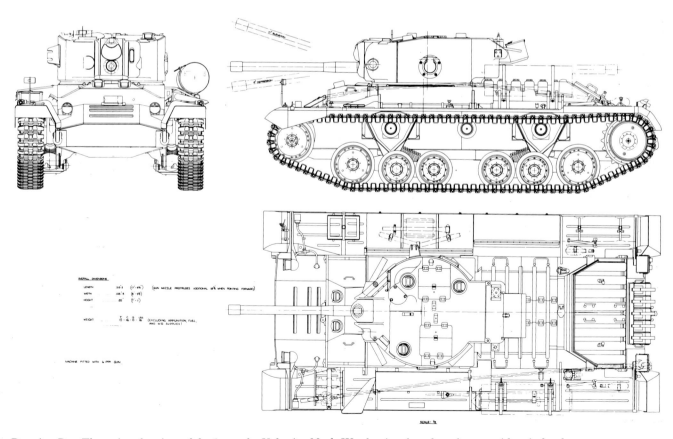

Drawing B: *Three-view drawings of the 6-pounder Valentine Mark IX, showing the enlarged turret with twin hatches.*

into the open breech of the 6-pounder, everything connected up, and the machine-gun could then be fired by the gunner, using the main gun-sights, down the barrel of the 6-pounder. No one could call the arrangement ideal, but apparently it worked quite well.

Turning now to the Crusader, it is clear that despite repeated and bitter complaints nothing had really improved. Airy reports from Britain might announce that production of Marks I and II had ceased in December 1942 and that, with the exception of those earmarked for conversion to other roles, the rest could now be scrapped, but as GHQ in the Middle East pointed out, their Mark Is were still being used for training and Mark IIs would have to remain in service until something better came along to replace them. Incidentally, one report from the same source explains that by this time it was general practice in the armoured regiments of the Eighth Army to fill auxiliary tanks with water instead of petrol, which was much more useful and a lot safer. It was also revealed that crews still equipped with early model Crusaders always went into action with the turret-top hatch, the so-called sunshine roof, wide open. This was regarded as the only way to escape in a hurry for the entire crew, but in any case the practice of going into action with the hatch open and the commander's head and shoulders visible above turret-level had almost become the rule in the Eighth Army, for reasons verging on bravado.

Those regiments of 6th Armoured Division just issued with the 6-pounder equipped Crusader Mark III must have been discomforted by the concurrent announcement by the War Office that it was now regarded as obsolescent. One local improvement reported at this time was the provision of home-made steel ammunition bins which, by protecting stowed rounds from hot shell splinters, at least reduced the risk of fire, but nothing could be done about the Crusader's reliability. As late as March 1943, the Eighth Army reported that of 717 Crusaders on its books, more than half were in unserviceable condition. There is good reason to suppose that most of the Crusaders supplied to 6th Armoured Division for service in Tunisia were of the Mark III type, but it is not clear from surviving records if they had adopted the practice apparently devised by 11th Armoured Division in Britain in December 1942. This was in connection with the two-man turret problem again. This division altered its establishment from a three to a four-tank troop structure, consisting of one 2-pounder Crusader and three with the 6-pounder. The former provided a suitable mount for the troop leader without actually reducing the maximum effective firepower of the troop. Towards the end of January 1943, the 16th/5th Lancers were informed that they would be converting to Shermans, followed by the other regiments of 26th Armoured Brigade. In fact, just as these arrived in mid-February, the Battle of Kasserine Pass began, in which green American troops failed in the face of a determined German attack and the regiment had to return

quickly to its old tanks and join, with the rest of the division, in a desperate struggle to prevent the Germans from gaining a major victory. With this dramatic event behind them, the regiments were gradually withdrawn until, by March, all were fully equipped with sixty-one of the new American tanks.

It is perhaps difficult to appreciate fully the delight British tank men felt upon receiving the Sherman. Many Eighth Army regiments had graduated to it through the Grant, and were pleased enough, but in 6th Armoured Division they were jumping straight from the Crusader and Valentine. To the 16th/5th Lancers, as their regimental history records, the Sherman seemed to have everything that mattered: thicker armour, a 75-mm (14 pdr) gun in place of the 2-pounder, and two diesel engines instead of one. What more could anyone ask? There is no doubt at all, and one may read it in any number of reports emanating from every quarter of what came to be known as the Mediterranean Theatre, that the Sherman immediately became a firm favourite with each British regiment with which it operated. The dual-purpose gun not only had the ability to deal, at last, with the pestilential German anti-tank guns by firing high explosive at them, it also had the range and hitting power to deal with German tanks such as the Panzer IV Special on their own terms. This last statement, however, requires a degree of qualification. In October 1942 a new 6-pounder round, the Armour-Piercing Capped, Ballistic Capped (APCBC) had entered service, and its performance against armour was far better than the projectile in the American gun. At 1,000 yards range, for example, the 6-pounder would penetrate 80 mm of armour, compared with 62 mm for the 75-mm gun. This made it much more effective, at modest ranges, against heavy tanks like the Tiger for instance, but even when one discounts the high explosive capability of the latter the 75-mm was preferred, since it would penetrate tanks like the Panzer III or IV at far greater ranges than the 6-pounder. Since one met these Panzers every day, and Tigers only rarely in Tunisia, the 75-mm was a universal favourite. The main complaint about the Sherman concerned the automatic gun stabiliser. Designed to permit accurate firing on the move, it appears not to have worked terribly well. This was not regarded as a serious problem, however, since the British had gradually abandoned this technique anyway, in favour of the German practice of stopping to fire. What counted most was that the Sherman had the full confidence of British tank crews. To quote the 16th/5th Lancers' history again, concerning the capture of the Fondouk Pass in April when 6th Armoured Division forced its way through a narrow defile in the face of a minefield, fifteen enemy anti-tank guns and possibly up to five Tigers, in a death or glory charge that cost the Division thirty-four tanks: 'Effective action at these long ranges was practicable with the Sherman tanks; but had been out of the question with Valentines.' It would be no exaggeration to claim that when General Montgomery spoke of the need for a universal tank, it was the Sherman that had inspired him.

For all his years of single-minded application to military service, General Montgomery's experience of armoured warfare, in practice, was very limited. Even his brother-in-law Percy Hobart, one of the most ardent converts to the creed of armoured warfare, had little influence, since it seems they did not get on. Granted tanks had been around since 1916, but until the desert war forced the issue, they were regarded as a specialist arm which nobody else, least of all the infantry, need associate with. Thus whatever it was that Montgomery really understood of the subject from first-hand experience was gleaned in the desert, an ideal landscape for the purpose, but not in any sense typical, at least for the Western Allies. It has to be supposed that when Montgomery expressed his views on the universal tank (see Introduction), as he had started to do even before Tripoli was taken, the opinion had germinated in the broad, barren reaches of Egypt and Libya, where it clearly made sense. Rolling hills covered in scrub-like vegetation, threaded by roads and tracks that channelled movement; large areas of permanent settlement and generally closer country, where sudden encounters could be expected at shorter ranges, and defence was more effective – these conditions would change things, and they were coming. Here, protection could be a greater asset than speed, or even a large gun, and the only Allied tank which fulfilled that requirement was the Churchill.

That its action debut at Dieppe was a disaster only added to its notoriety, but that was hardly the Churchill's fault. Of course the Churchill had lost its credibility even before then and, bearing in mind the equally sorry sagas of Covenanter and Crusader, the latter still being acted out in 1943, it seems fair to assume that soldiers and statesmen were prepared to believe anything about British tanks so long as it was bad. In October 1942 a Most Secret report from the Tank Board in Britain had listed the Churchill as 'obsolescent and going out of production' and it had hardly fired a shot in anger by then. At the same time a major rework programme was under way by Broom and Wade of High Wycombe and the production parents for the type, Vauxhall Motors.

Late in January 1943, under pressure from many sub-contractors who believed business would suffer if production ceased, the War Cabinet approved construction of a further 500 Churchills. It was a typical British response of the time, only in this case a reasonably fortuitous one. By that time the War Office had reached a momentous decision, at least for British tanks, that the Churchill should go to the war. Whether, as some claim, this was decided entirely on the results of Alamein, where six Churchills had done moderately well, or as seems more likely because there were some 3,000 of them in Britain, many in the hands of trained regiments itching to use them, is not clear. Whatever the explanation, six Churchill regiments were already on the high seas, with course set

for North Africa. First to arrive, in Algiers, were 142nd RAC in late January 1943, followed by 51 RTR and the North Irish Horse; they formed the 25th Army Tank Brigade. In March, the 21st Army Tank Brigade arrived: 12th RTR, 48th RTR and 145th RAC. Some 300 Churchills were available for service in Tunisia, including Marks I, II and III.

The Churchill was not the only new arrival in Tunisia. Some time earlier, in late November 1942, a ship had docked at Bizerta and unloaded three of the massive Panzer VI, Tiger tanks soon to make a reputation of almost mythical proportions that hypnotised Allied soldiers at all levels. In due course there were more of them, companies from 501st and 504th Heavy Tank Battalions which, originally, had been intended to join Rommel's Afrika Korps. Typically now, when it was too late to rescue the situation, Hitler revealed that inflexible trait of stubbornness which would lose him much valuable equipment, thousands of good men, and ultimately the war. Only inevitable defeat, it seems, was ever reinforced.

There is not a lot to be gained by comparing the two tanks, except to say that in terms of frontal armour thickness there was relatively little to choose between them. In every other respect they were totally different. More significant is what they represented. From the outset, particularly with the Panzers III and IV, the Germans had grown used to reliability. Their tanks also had the magic ingredient of stretch potential, which is to say that they could take improvements in weapon size and armour thickness without seriously compromising either performance or reliability. In this sense they kept ahead of the Allies, and might even be said to have been bear-leading them into making improvements which otherwise might not have qualified for consideration. Working from this secure base the Germans had now been tempted into making a quantum leap which, for the time, was not justified; in doing so they sacrificed their other magic ingredient, reliability. And reliability was still the British grail. Bigger guns and thicker armour were desirable, indeed essential in due course, but until the problem of chronic unreliability – which at this time was affecting six different British-designed tanks – could be overcome, there was no point in worrying about anything else. American input would alleviate the reliability quandary for the time being, and within twelve months the British would remedy it, but they would never even draw level with Germany in the gun or armour race.

It is not necessary to record the actions of the six Churchill regiments in Tunisia – that has already been skilfully done elsewhere.* Suffice it to say that the majority of them put up performances that would have surprised their critics. They accounted for at least three Tigers, albeit at considerable cost to themselves and, in the

---

B Perrett, *The Churchill*, Ian Allan, 1974.

famous action at Steamroller Farm, scaled what a German commander called 'impossible heights'. Not that taking out Tigers was always a matter of power or great sacrifice. Luck had a lot to do with it. Early in April, following the Battle of Wadi Akarit, two Daimler armoured cars of 11th Hussars encountered a Tiger. One held its attention – under fire – while the other stalked it on the flank to within 500 yards before opening fire, at which point the Tiger's crew baled out and surrendered. It was not quite the victory it seemed – the tank was immobile, having been disabled earlier, but the armoured car crews had not known that when they began the stalk, and an 88-mm gun is an 88-mm gun. It is worth remarking that a report from the Eighth Army (was this the voice of Montgomery?) actually used this incident to support the view that heavily armoured tanks were unnecessary, claiming instead that, even in Europe lighter, more mobile tanks would always have the edge. They said nothing about the advantages of superiority in numbers being a vital contributory factor in these circumstances; perhaps this was taken for granted.

Surviving evidence suggests that the men of the 21st and 25th Tank Brigades had a lot more faith in their Churchills than one might be led to expect from their history, but this was the result of knowledge. Living and working with the tanks over a long period, these men were used to their awkward ways. Such familiarity means that crews will recognise trouble, and even anticipate it, before a serious breakdown occurs, which is more than half the battle. Secure behind thick armour, they went out to Tunisia full of confidence, although the extent to which this was justified is another matter.

In the case of the 21st Army Tank Brigade, this confidence could be described as surprising. In the summer of 1942, while still in Britain, the three regiments from this brigade had each supplied one squadron of Churchills for an experimental exercise codenamed Trent, the object of which was to test a random selection of twenty-five reworked tanks. The intention was to run the Churchills for 1,000 miles over a six-week period in the hills around Hawick in southern Scotland. Ideally there would be an adequate mixture of road and cross-country running, but the War Office cut the trial short, so most of the mileage had to be made up on the roads. One tank was withdrawn following an accident, but of the remainder only eight failed to make up the total mileage. However, during the trial there were 144 instances of engine failure, 122 of brake failure and in all, 516 cases of stoppages due to one or more causes, and that with regular daily maintenance by squadron fitters.

One important feature that the Churchill could not accept was protected ammunition stowage. It was considered, but the view was that it would only be possible with a substantial reduction in the amount of ammunition carried, which was not acceptable, as a report dated March 1943 explained. In that same report it was announced that the Experimental Wing of the Gunnery School at Lul-worth had developed a new type of Churchill, the Mark ICS, or Close Support version. A conventional Mark I Churchill had a 3-inch howitzer in the hull front, in addition to the 2-pounder in the turret. What Lulworth had done was to swap these two weapons around; not a difficult operation, since the mountings were more or less interchangeable anyway. By locating the howitzer in the turret such a tank was able to dish out smoke or HE in all directions, but quite how much use could be found for a 2-pounder in the hull, with such limited traverse, is difficult to imagine. The Gunnery School produced drawings that enabled the conversion to be carried out in all theatres of operation, but the extent to which it was actually done is not clear. In Tunisia the Churchill earned its reprieve, even if British industry had initiated it. In London on 14 May 1943 an order was placed for 1,000 more, supported by an agreement that production would continue throughout 1944.

The fighting in North Africa ended on 13 May 1943, following the surrender of all remaining Axis forces. In the three years since it had begun, a great deal had been learnt by all sides on the realities of tank fighting and, naturally, on matters of tank design. The British experience was summed up in a Most Secret cipher telegram sent to the Chief of the Imperial General Staff in London on 18 May by his deputy, who was then visiting Tunisia. He had canvassed the opinions of every British commander in the field from Brigadier 'Pip' Roberts to General Sir Oliver Leese, as well as the resident tank experts, and had found a strong view in favour of the dual-purpose tank gun, preferably with a calibre of not less than 75-mm. Armoured brigades of armoured divisions, most of which were now equipped with Shermans, were adamant, some commanders claiming that they would prefer 100 per cent 75-mm, more especially after the fighting in Tunisia compared with the desert. Presumably among those who held this view were the commanders of 6th Armoured Division following the battle at Hamman Lif (referred to in the telegram as the 'final débâcle') on 9 May. Here the tanks had been confined to a 300-yard wide gap between the hills and the sea, which had been heavily defended by 88-mm anti-aircraft guns. Overlooked by British infantry positions and pounded by artillery, this strong defensive position had been taken by tanks virtually driving through the surf and treating the guns as they passed to a barrage of 75-mm HE fire. This effectively convinced the Germans that their last defensive position in Tunisia, at Enfidaville, was now compromised.

Yet it is clear from the tone of the telegram that influential elements in Britain were still promoting the 6-pounder, especially now that it could be supplied with the highly effective APCBC round and a high-explosive shell. Few commanders on the spot were prepared to accept more than two 6-pounder tanks per squadron, for the advantage which the APCBC round possessed against thick armour applied only at shorter ranges, while the HE round was dismissed as all but useless, compared with the 75-mm. One could not take out an anti-tank gun crew except with a very close hit, while the shell had no delayed action fuse and would not detonate with a graze shot. Moving on to army tank brigades, with their infantry tanks, the DCIGS found more approval for the 6-pounder HE and greater interest in the penetrative power of APCBC, but still a strong preference for the dual-purpose 75-mm (which, it should be remembered, they had not yet experienced). Summing up, the DCIGS recommended that armoured brigades should be equipped in the proportion 30 per cent 6-pounder, 60 per cent 75-mm, and 10 per cent close support, while in army tank brigades the quantities of 6-pounder and 75-mm should be reversed. Finally, he told the CIGS: 'You are aware that Montgomery believes in the Universal Tank (Sherman or better) and would have all his Armd. Bdes. (including Army Tank Bdes.) on the same basis.'

While the opinions of the great and the good, such as General Montgomery, were assiduously canvassed, recorded and doubtless heeded where it mattered, it would be surprising if they reflected the views held at all levels in the command structure. It is therefore refreshing to discover that in at least one instance, towards the end of the North African campaign, a serious attempt was made to gather the views of three officers with more direct experience of tank warfare. Between them these three men, Captain R E Gregory of the Greys, Captain R G Shattock of 3rd Royal Tank Regiment, and a Captain R B Brown whose regiment is not recorded, represented user-opinion across the board since, to judge from their comments, they had first-hand knowledge of virtually every tank and tank gun in British service at that time. In most instances their views were in close harmony, although they were invited to comment on a whole series of subjects, but where they differ it would probably be fair to ascribe it to a penchant for the tank they had had most experience of, or most success in.

Where guns were concerned, Captain Shattock had most to say. He was totally sold on the 75-mm, which he regarded as the minimum calibre for future medium tanks because he considered high-explosive capability essential. He was also quite happy with the 6-pounder, although he commented that poor clearance in the mounting often caused it to jam during running out after recoil. One odd contrast was his liking for the American 37-mm gun – although he regarded it as a waste of money in the Grant, since it was never used – compared with the 2-pounder, which he considered obsolete. Bearing in mind that he came from a regiment that had been equipped with American tanks since late 1941, it is difficult to understand what his opinion of British guns was based on, and one may suspect an element of hearsay in his evidence. On paper, at least, the 2-pounder had a slightly better performance. Captain Gregory did not like anti-aircraft machine-guns because they stuck up in the air and gave

the tank's position away, although he admitted that they were handy to have mounted when tanks were in leaguer. His opinion seems to have been shared by most British tank officers, although another factor against a cupola mounting was that it got in the way when one was getting out in a hurry. Gregory felt that a better arrangement would be to have the front-hull, or lap gun as he called it, made suitable for mounting as an anti-aircraft weapon when the need arose.

On the subject of gun controls Captain Brown realised that geared elevation would be essential as weapons got heavier, although he felt it would hamper flexible use of the coaxial machine-gun. What is odd is the revelation that none of the officers were that sold on powered traverse. They were happy that most types worked efficiently, and again appreciated that as turrets got heavier, powered traverse would be necessary, but Gregory pointed out that his men preferred manual traverse for picking up a target. On sights they could not agree. Brown favoured a telescope, Shattock thought the American periscope sight was very bad, yet Gregory liked it best of all for its wide field of view. Even so he regarded German sights as better than any of them. Both Brown and Shattock had been in tanks with gyro stabilisers, and agreed that they never used them.

Based on experience in the desert, Captain Gregory called for thicker frontal armour, while Shattock claimed that pistol ports and vision slits should be done away with. He reckoned they were never used and only created weak spots. He also claimed that the armour on the Crusader was useless, since it could be penetrated by a 50-mm round at ranges up to 1,500 yards. In his view the tank was only suitable for reconnaissance. On the subject of tank engines, however, he immediately contradicted this assertion, reiterating all the usual complaints about the Crusader and describing the air cleaners as hopelessly inadequate and badly positioned. Ingress of dirt led to excessive piston wear and this, in turn, caused a loss of power and smoky exhaust due to burnt oil. Loss of power caused poor manœuvrability in heavy going which, he said, could prove fatal, while exhaust smoke gave the tank's position away and rendered it useless for reconnaissance. Gregory thought that the clutch was the Stuart tank's weak feature, while the radial engine in Grants and Shermans was fine up to 150 hours' running and then started to use oil heavily. He pointed out that tank crews were often too tired to carry out a thorough maintenance programme in leaguer and added that only a thing that could be done easily got done. Shattock agreed on medium tank engines, but regarded the Stuart engine as the most reliable of all. It would give a phenomenal mileage with the absolute minimum of attention and, because of the high power-to-weight ratio, made the tank ideal for reconnaissance. Gregory was the only one with enough experience of the GMC diesels in Shermans to comment. He liked the set-up for its reliability and performance and made the point that crews felt a lot happier without gallons of high-octane petrol in their vehicles, although he understood that this was not a major cause of fires.

Generally everyone was quite happy with most types of gearbox and transmission, although Shattock again complained about the Crusader, with good reason. On the other hand there was general agreement that the Christie suspension on the Crusader gave the best ride and gun platform, although they had no specific complaints about the American system. On the subject of general tank design Captain Gregory was the only officer to make any worthwhile observations. He appreciated the need for a fast light tank, although he felt that the Stuart was too high. He saw no need for heavy assault tanks and seemed happy to settle for something that would get along at a maximum of 25 mph which had moderately good armour. He believed that a tank with massively thick armour was still vulnerable from its exposed tracks and pointed out that a tank which was stopped with a shattered track was just as effectively knocked out for the duration of that battle as one that had blown up. In his experience the Sherman, or something like it, was quite good enough and he explained that in his regiment a number of Shermans had been struck by 88-mm rounds and suffered nothing worse than a bit of armour chewed out.

All three officers were anxious to stress the need for simplicity, ease of access for maintenance, and robust construction – all features in which the American tanks excelled. Brown made an interesting point when he said that commanders of armoured formations were very wary of committing tanks to battle unless they all had sufficient fuel on board. He knew of cases where an attack had been held up for as much as two hours while this was attended to, when time had been of the greatest tactical importance. He was also troubled by the practice of changing equipment in the field, and cited the example of a regiment which exchanged petrol-driven tanks for diesels without either the crews or workshop staff being given any training whatsoever – they had been left to learn from experience and during that time could not get the best results from their vehicles.

Modest as it was, the success of a few Matilda Scorpion flail tanks at El Alamein had not been forgotten. Indeed, it tended to be magnified as time went by, so when consideration was being given to a formal attack on the Mareth Line they were included in the battle plan. The intervening months had been devoted to consideration of the requirements for such tanks and the formation of No 1 Scorpion Regiment and two independent squadrons to operate them. The first need to be identified was greater speed – not during flailing, that would only lead to mines being missed by the flails or detonated as the tank passed over them – rather, it was essential that they should move faster between minefields, to offset the paucity of numbers. Middle East Command had asked for permission to convert 500 tanks, but the most that the War Office would sanction was 300 and it is unlikely that even this number actually appeared. A Scorpion Mark III was therefore developed, based on the Grant tank. It had the same flail rotor, lattice girder jib and Ford V8 engine as the Matilda version but was of lighter construction and with an improved drive train. The flail operator was located inside the hull, but since the attachments masked the 75-mm gun, this was taken out. Indeed the first Grant Scorpions also had their 37-mm turrets removed, presumably to save weight, and the aperture plated over with a panel that incorporated an escape hatch and a small, box-shaped observation turret.

C Squadron collected their Grants from Tripoli in March 1943, yet it was A Squadron, still in Matildas, which took part in the Mareth battle on 20 March, with only moderate success. In addition to flails the regiment

8 *The original pattern of Grant Scorpion flail, in which a small box replaced the 37-mm turret.*

had some Valentines equipped with anti-mine rollers which, being less prone to wear, were used initially to determine the limits of the minefield. They also had some Porcupine-type spiked concrete rollers that were trailed behind the tanks to deal with anti-personnel S-mines (or Schuh-Minen). Although they had not seen action, the Grants were clearly thought to be vulnerable by their crews because there is a report of the observation turret and escape hatch being bolstered up with sandbags and disused petrol cans. At the same time a new terminology came into being. Crews spoke of 'Scorping' a piece of ground which, when it was done, had been 'Scorped', while officers discussed the number of mines they had 'put up', as if they were quail. A Squadron got their Grants early in April, although again it was B Squadron, who still had Matildas, which was called up for action at Wadi Akarit on 5 April.

On 18 April it was announced that six Grant turrets had arrived for fitting, so clearly it had now been decided to give the tanks some teeth, even if it was only a 37-mm gun and coaxial Browning. Bearing in mind that the end of a successful flailing run placed them on the wrong side of an enemy minefield, ahead of everyone else, it does not appear unreasonable that they should have needed some-

thing to shoot with. On 19 April A Squadron took Grant Scorpions into action for the first time, presumably in their turretless form, since there would not have been time to fit them. After a four-day operation they reported greater structural damage to the flail equipment, putting it down to the rigid attachment of the jib to the tank, instead of the trunnion mount employed on the Matilda, which had a bit of give in it.

Meanwhile back in Egypt 400 and 401 Independent Scorpion Squadrons were engaged in various experiments, the results of which will be explained in the next chapter. In July 1943 400 Squadron reported having two Valentine III pilot tanks, presumably meaning anti-mine rollers, two Porcupines and some Bangalore torpedos, of which more shortly. In August they reported receiving twelve Grant Scorpions, which must have been of the turretless type to judge from a sketch in their War Diary. Again on the subject of terminology it is interesting to find this unit describing as Donkey Engines what others called Flail Engines. In November 1943 400 Squadron went across to India while 401 remained in Egypt on experimental work.

It is worth remarking that all the design and production work for this device was undertaken by REME base workshops in North Africa. However, with the forthcoming invasions of Sicily and Italy in mind, attempts were made by HQ in Cairo to have suitable flail tanks supplied from Britain, since a need for greater numbers was anticipated. The specific request, forwarded to the War Office, was for a version of the Baron flail device fitted to M5 Stuart and M4 Sherman tanks. It was estimated that thirty would be required, but the plea was turned down by London who explained that the system could not be adapted to other types of tank. It had been designed around the Matilda and in any case none of them would be available before June 1943.

9 *Turreted Grant Scorpion flails in hilly country. In this view the auxilliary engine housing can be seen.*

Few other tank-based special devices appear to have been considered for use in Tunisia. Versions of the Anti-Mine Roller Attachment and Snake explosive device were certainly available but the only other locally produced contraption, known from a single photograph, was a flimsy looking tubular steel attachment pivoted to the nose of an AEC Mark I armoured car. It had a central sprung skid on the outer end and two loops at the extremities of a cross-bar which looked as if they were intended to trail small rollers ahead of each wheel. The fact that protective panels are hanging in front of each tyre suggests that some sort of blast was anticipated, but it does not look as if the equipment would have survived such treatment for very long.

2 One tank for Italy

The Allied landings in Sicily (10 July 1943) and at Calabria on the toe of mainland Italy (3 September 1943), along with the surrender of Italy, were major landmarks on the path to victory. Although the actual landings, in both instances, were relatively unopposed, this did not last. Sicily was by no means a pushover and it was bad tank country which the Germans, in particular, used well. The lesson that the days of desert warfare were well and truly over now hit home, and in a surprising way.

Tank commanders learned, by their comrades' misfortunes, that it was no longer wise to go into action with important parts of the anatomy on show. Indeed, it is claimed that German snipers became so adept in close country that even a few fingers visible on the rim of the commander's hatch were liable to be shot off. Casualties soon reached alarming proportions and suddenly everyone was calling for cupolas again. As explained in the previous volume of this work (*The Great Tank Scandal*, p 31), cupolas of the type found on early British cruiser tanks had got themselves a very bad name, due mainly to scare stories. Largely apocryphal, these told of commanders being decapitated when enemy fire swept cupolas clean off turrets, but they did not need to be true to be believed, so the fittings were not to be found on any British tank built after 1940. American designers had not used them on the Sherman either, but whether this was due to British influence or not it is impossible to confirm. A large cupola, complete with machine gun, had been a feature of the M3 Lee but not of its Anglicised counterpart, the Grant, and this may have had some bearing on the matter. Closed down in a tank without a cupola, the commander is little better off than the rest of his crew. Granted he is provided with a revolving periscope, but it is a laborious thing to use, giving a very narrow field of vision and making it very easy for him to lose his bearings. In fact early cupolas were little better in this respect, providing a bit more headroom but precious little in the way of all-round vision. The Germans were, and always had been, well ahead in this aspect of tank design, as in many others. However, here, as in all things, there were stages of development, fashions almost, which seemed to be shared even across the divide of war. The Germans introduced a new style in the summer of 1943; the American Direct Vision Cupola was adopted in the spring of 1944, contemporary with the British All-Round Vision Cupola. All had one feature in common, a series of vision ports all around the rim of the cupola fitted either with direct vision blocks, in the case of the American pattern, or periscopes in the other two. All

10   *The British All-Round Vision Cupola Mark II installed on a Sherman turret. Notice the three forward-looking persicopes and the adaptor ring which locates it within the original hatch.*

of them gave a commander the opportunity to scan the battlefield all around his tank in safety, although his ability to see clearly was diminished by the limitations of the glass and the limited field of view each one provided. In this respect the later British version, the All-Round Vision Cupola Mark II, was probably the best. It had been developed by a Dr Pochin of the Medical Research Council, based at Lulworth, and produced by the Department of Tank Design. It featured eight periscopes arranged around the raised lip of the cupola, although a cluster of three, which normally faced forwards, were placed as close together as possible to give the tank commander a wider field of view in any one direction. The remaining five periscopes covered all other angles of bearing, but the rearmost one also had the ability to swing, so that some elevation and depression could be obtained. The two-piece hatch that covered the top of the cupola was designed in such a way that it assisted the commander to view the world in some safety. With both flaps raised to the vertical position he was protected from the sides, but it was also possible to raise both hatches in their 'closed' position, to create a narrow slit above the top of the periscopes through which a clearer all-round view could be obtained. Finally, and uniquely, the British cupola could be rotated independently of the turret through 360 degrees, a feature the Americans wished to introduce on their next version. Since it was intended to fit existing Cromwell and Churchill turrets, the ARV cupola was rather small, and very restricted as an escape hatch. This is

11　*A Sherman III (M4A2) of B Squadron, 44th RTR near the River Sangro. The stowage tray on the side of the rear deck has been formed from the end sections of the trackguard.*

what the Americans did not like about it. Even so it was fitted to British Shermans, with the aid of an adaptor ring.

The title of this chapter is true only in a very general sense, if one is happy to overlook the presence of Stuarts in the reconnaissance role and Grants fulfilling some subordinate functions such as command and flail tanks. Shermans were certainly the only fighting tanks used by all Allied armoured regiments early on in the Italian campaign. The difficult question is the extent to which this was due to policy or to circumstances. In the case of the United States Army the answer must be the latter because Shermans (and their kin, the tank destroyers) were all they had. In the Canadian Army it was a matter of policy. Although many Canadian armoured regiments had trained on Churchills in Britain, and of course used them on the Dieppe raid, it is clear from their Official History that they had little faith in the tank. It was not the Churchill's questionable reliability that troubled the Canadians, but its guns. The British 2-pounder was almost beneath notice, and they had little to say in favour of the 6-pounder either, all of which must have affected the view they had of their own medium tank, the Ram. These were now arriving in Britain in quantity, and being used to replace the Churchills, but they too had been designed

around the British guns. Technically there was no good reason why this tank could not have been fitted with the American 75-mm, except that there were now enough Shermans pouring out of the United States arsenals for everyone, so that converting the Rams would be largely a waste of time. The real question hangs over British attitudes, and it is simply a matter of who one is prepared to believe. Some official documents claim that the only reason all British regiments committed to Sicily and Italy in the early stages had Shermans was because the 21st and 25th Army Tank Brigades, with their Churchills, had taken such a battering in Tunisia that they needed more time to recuperate and make up for losses in tanks and men. One might ask why the 23rd Armoured Brigade, which was trained in the infantry tank role, had not exchanged their Valentines for Churchills instead of Shermans if that was the case, but it would be difficult to supply a satisfactory answer. An alternative explanation is offered in a paper entitled 'AFVs in the Mediterranean Theatre', compiled by Lieutenant-Colonel F W S Gordon-Hall in 1945. According to this source the reason was topographical. Intelligence revealed, as the British Official History puts it, that 'The roads, coastal and interior, twist and turn, and abound in bridges, viaducts, culverts and tunnels' on the Aspromonte plateau which forms the toe of Calabria. Since tanks were to be used it made sense to employ 30-ton Shermans instead of 40-ton Churchills, at least as far as the bridges, viaducts and culverts were concerned. The twists and turns were another matter: as we shall see later, the Shermans, with their relatively crude Cletrac steering systems, found very tight corners something of a problem, often having to reverse a couple of times to get around. Such things were nothing to a Churchill with its Merritt-Brown transmission that enabled it to spin on the spot. The third possibility, which it would now be impossible to confirm, is the Montgomery factor. Was this his command decision in pursuance of the Universal Tank theory? Not that there were any complaints, whatever the reason. An official report by 6th Armoured Division which, it will be remembered, arrived in Tunisia with a mixture of Crusaders and Valentines, confirmed that the all-Sherman regiment of sixty-one tanks was entirely satisfactory. Training was simplified, as was workshop practice and the supply of spares, but most important of all the regiments had good hitting power and, the report concluded, 'no disadvantage can be found with this principle'. Since they have been mentioned it is worth just rubbing in the point that no Crusaders would go to Italy because their stock with tank crews was so low, while the Valentine, although reliable and available, was so cramped once the 6-pounder gun had been installed, as to be almost unfightable. Therefore, in the summer of 1943 the British Army went into action in a theatre which, for the next twelve months, would see its most concentrated war effort, without any British-made tanks in its armoured regiments at all.

Yet the real problem now was not tanks but the country. Italy simply did not have the configuration to suit tank fighting. As another report put it, 'due to the mountainous nature of the country armour could not be used on a large scale'. If it wasn't the mountains, then the streams and rivers that descended from them formed a succession of obstacles, and even the cultivated plains were little better. Crops such as vines and tobacco often stood tall enough to obscure the immediate view and sometimes meant that a tank's hull machine gunner had a better idea of what was going on than its commander. Here British crews previously used to Crusaders discovered one advantage they had over Shermans. The hull and turret machine-guns in the latter were .30 calibre Brownings, which did not have the stamina of British Besas and also lacked the telescopic sights built into their mountings which were a feature of most British-built tanks. For general prophylactic fire, when it was just a matter of spraying ammunition everywhere, the Browning was good enough, but if you really wanted to hit something then you stood a much better change with an aimed burst from a Besa.

For the Germans the worst disadvantage was the political change. The fall of Mussolini and subsequent surrender of the Badoglio government now meant that they were operating in an occupied country, with all that implies; to make matters worse, in October of 1943 the Italians were to join the Allies (albeit with the nice distinction of co-belligerent, rather than ally). From a combat point of view the mountains and rivers proved eminently defensible and handed every advantage to heavily armoured tanks like the Tiger, as well as the many varieties of self-propelled anti-tank gun which they developed. Although technically vulnerable to amphibious flank attacks such as at Salerno and later Anzio, these were expensive and complex operations to mount and subsequently became impossible when resources were diverted to northern Europe.

For the Allies, in these conditions, good reconnaissance was considered vital and armoured car regiments developed special techniques and organisations to suit. A typical squadron would comprise three scout car troops, with Daimler Dingoes for preference and three armoured car troops employing Daimlers, Humbers or later Staghounds. Then there would be a support troop using White Scout Cars to carry assault personnel, a heavy troop to give back-up fire and, of course a headquarters troop. The matter of a heavy troop was first raised in Tunisia when the closer nature of the country made reconnaissance a far more risky business. An early attempt was made by replacing the 2-pounder in an AEC Mark I armoured car with a 3-inch howitzer, but this was dropped when somebody caught sight of an American equipment, a White half-track mounting a 75-mm gun. Two were borrowed from the Americans for trials and found to be ideal. They were mobile enough to keep up with armoured cars under most conditions, big enough to carry the gun and a fair stock of ammunition yet, with their tracks, easily able to get off the road quickly and take up good fire support positions as required. Similar half-tracks, without the guns, were also being adopted by British infantry motor battalions to replace their 15-cwt platoon trucks, the American vehicles having a much better performance across country, as well as the advantage of some armour protection.

12 M3 (75-mm) half-tracks belonging to the heavy troop of 56th Reconnaissance Regiment in Italy.

Experience with different types of armoured cars was better recorded in Italy than elsewhere, and some of the points raised are worth studying. The Daimler, of course, needs little comment. Once crews got used to them they were highly popular and set a standard by which all others were judged. Since they did not have a clutch in the normal sense they did not suffer from the wear problems associated with other makes, but they still created problems of their own. One report described Italian mud as the best, the most glutinous and the deepest of any in the world. When a conventional armoured car got bogged, the clutch was invariably the first thing to suffer when the driver tried to get it out. However, in order to achieve the same ends the dirver of a Daimler would treat his fluid flywheel like a torque converter, doing even more damage.

13 A Staghound, leading a Sherman on parade. The armoured car has an ammunition box let into the offside mudguard. The markings indicate 40th RTR, 23rd Armoured Brigade, which was issued with some armoured cars towards the end of the war in Greece.

14 An AEC Mark II showing the large, welded turret designed to accommodate the 6-pounder gun.

When the Staghound arrived crews compared it unfavourably with the Daimler. Early mechanical problems did not help, but the real complaint was its size. Since it weighed 12 tons to the Daimler's 7, people could not see why it should only mount a 37-mm gun, which was only just comparable to the Daimler's 2-pounder. Even so, it gained in popularity particularly because it was powerful and easy to drive. The New Zealanders in Italy modified some to a close support version by fitting a 3-inch howitzer in place of the 37-mm; in this form it was known as the Staghound II. Their other favourite modification was to build a pair of 25-pounder ammunition boxes into the front wings, in which they kept tyre chains for use in the notorious Italian mud.

The Humber armoured cars remained surprisingly popular, although the three-man turret in the Mark III version was considered too cramped and there were complaints that the driver's hatch was too small to escape through in an emergency. The strangest thing concerned its main armament, the 15-mm Besa gun. This was cordially disliked all round, for a variety of reasons. The Besa was fed from a 25-round metal belt, so long bursts of sustained fire could not be achieved. Even if they could have been, it was quite impossible to fire accurately on automatic because the long barrel had a tendency to whiplash, an action which it transmitted to the mounting, so that ammunition was simply wasted. Instead it was invariably used as a single-shot weapon when required. From a maintenance point of view it was a very difficult gun to load, and clearing stoppages was a nightmare; worst of all, however, it was nearly three times as heavy as its 7.92-mm counterpart and was therefore very hard work to strip and clean. The Humber Mark IV with the 37-mm gun only attracted minor criticisms by comparison. An improved escape hatch had been designed for the driver, but the complaint now was that the car no longer had a reverse steering facility. Faults were also discovered in the gun mounting, and cracks appeared in the armour. Despite the fact that these cars had Runflat tyres which could be trusted to remain sound for a reasonable period after being punctured, there was soon a demand for a spare wheel. This was normally mounted on a bracket welded to the car's side hull escape door, making it very heavy to handle, and this was also objected to.

The Mark II version of the big AEC Armoured Car also saw service in Italy. Its size always made it unpopular because it was difficult to conceal and very awkward to handle in restricted conditions, although the 6-pounder gun was welcomed. Where the AEC was outstanding, compared with all other armoured cars, was reliability. From mileage returns by units it soon became clear that on average AECs, with their big diesel engines, were achieving 10,000 miles between breakdowns where most other types were not doing better than 6,000 miles. At least it would have made them popular with REME workshops. One of the most promising armoured cars of the entire

15 An M8 Greyhound armoured car in British service, shown with the side mudguards removed. This vehicle also seems to have belonged to 40th RTR.

campaign never saw much active service with British units. This was the American M8 Greyhound, the only six-wheeled armoured car employed by the Western Allies. A number were issued to British troops in the theatre, but their use was forbidden by the General Staff in London because British investigators reported that the hull floor plates were too thin to withstand mine-blast. Thus no published comments appeared upon their performance, although a British report compiled in Italy at the end of the war recorded that a fair number operated by the US Fifth Army could be found, dotted about northern Italy, suffering from battle damage. It is interesting to note that the writer did not ascribe this to faults in the Greyhound's design, despite its apparent vulnerability and open top turret. Rather he regarded it as a tribute to the sacrifice that reconnaissance troops, no matter what their nationality, accepted as a part of the job. Having produced extra belly armour plates as a quick-fit package in Britain and shipped them out to Italy, it was decided that stronger front springs would now be required. These were so slow in coming that some units got fed up with waiting and ran a few Greyhounds on the standard springs, without any apparent ill effects. The 2nd Derbyshire Yeomanry had some Greyhounds in Austria at the very end of the war and they recorded a very strange problem – recurring punctures in the rearmost set of tyres. Investigations seemed to reveal that these were caused by discarded rounds of small arms ammunition, flicked into the upright position by the leading rear wheel and then caught, point uppermost, the rear one. When it was pointed out that the same thing was not found on other types of six-wheeled vehicle, the explanation given was that it was due to the close spacing on the Greyhound's rear bogie.

Returning briefly to the subject of Daimler Scout Cars, it is worth recording that in the summer of 1943 these underwent a significant change. Experience in service showed them to be very vulnerable to mines, and there were demands for a thicker armoured floor. While this need was appreciated, the authorities in Britain seemed loath to abandon the idea of an armoured roof which, although it had been modified in its action since the first model, was regarded as a nuisance by most crews and was rarely used. When the message finally got through, the little car appeared with a simple canvas cover in place of the roof and this saving in weight enabled the floor to be thickened. Whether this really did much good in a practical sense is another matter. Striking a mine in a Daimler Dingo was still normally regarded as fatal for both crew members. Operational experience showed the extent to which terrain dictated tactics. In mountainous regions, according to one report, it was found advisable for a Dingo to take the lead, while in open country it was much wiser to have some firepower up front. In that case a Daimler armoured car would lead the way, which led to further excitement. It was learned that German anti-tank gunners would lay down smoke before retiring, and some adventurous troop leaders adopted the practise of charging through the smoke to pick off the retreating gun and its crew. This might work once or twice, but it is unwise to rely on such ploys indefinitely. As the same report pointed out, the Germans were likely to stay on the third occasion and then it was 'goodbye troop leader'. Conditions in Italy meant that it was rare for an armoured car regiment to function as a whole. Detached squadrons were the general rule and this demanded much closer liaison with other arms to ensure that information was passed on.

On the subject of reconnaissance there had been similar developments in British tank regiments. When first supplied, the M3 Stuart light tanks had been used mainly as cruisers since, in terms of firepower and protection, they came close to matching the A13s and Crusaders then in use, while beating both hands down in terms of reliability. With the arrival of the Sherman they were soon relegated to reconnaissance duties and suffered a drop in popularity when the next model, the M3A1 or Stuart Mark III appeared. Outwardly similar to the earlier model it featured a turret basket and floor which, to British users, rendered it unfightable. This showed up one of the most serious faults in United States tank design during the war, the combination of a rear-mounted engine with front-end transmission and track-driving sprockets. Besides being inefficient in a purely mechanical sense, since it places the top run of the track in tension, the arrangement can create awkward internal problems. No matter how you arrange it, the engine has to be linked to its gearbox somehow, and this means a driveshaft running smack through the middle of the fighting compartment. In larger tanks this does not matter too much (it is worth remembering that most German tanks of the period had the same layout, without

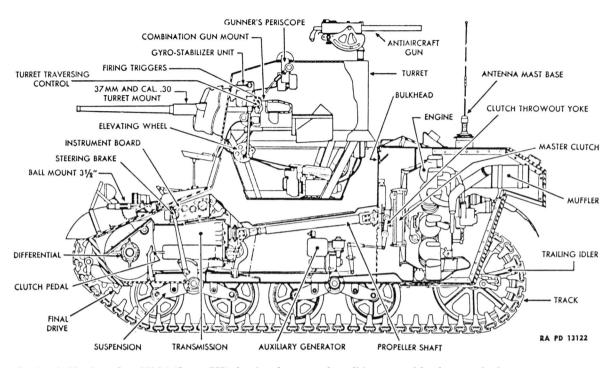

GUNNER'S PERISCOPE
COMBINATION GUN MOUNT
GYRO-STABILIZER UNIT
FIRING TRIGGERS
TURRET TRAVERSING CONTROL
37 MM AND CAL. .30 TURRET MOUNT
ELEVATING WHEEL
INSTRUMENT BOARD
STEERING BRAKE
BALL MOUNT 3½"
DIFFERENTIAL
CLUTCH PEDAL
FINAL DRIVE
SUSPENSION
TRANSMISSION
AUXILIARY GENERATOR
PROPELLER SHAFT
ANTIAIRCRAFT GUN
TURRET
BULKHEAD
ENGINE
ANTENNA MAST BASE
CLUTCH THROWOUT YOKE
MASTER CLUTCH
MUFFLER
TRAILING IDLER
TRACK
RA PD 13122

Drawing C: *Sectioned side view of an M3A1 (Stuart III) showing the cramped conditions created by the turret basket.*

suffering any serious problems) but in a small tank it is not so clever. Space is always at a premium anyway, and if, like the early Stuarts, the tank has an upright radial engine the driveshaft enters the crew compartment at an impossible height which cannot be ignored. In the Stuart Mark I, which did not have a turret basket, the crew learned to live with the inconvenience. There is evidence to suggest that they avoided turning the turret if at all possible, relying instead upon the limited traverse for the main armament built into the mounting. Matters got worse when some late production M3 tanks arrived in Britain equipped with M3A1 turrets.

Now lacking free movement of the gun within the turret, they had to rely on teamwork. With the gunner unable to reach the traversing handle, which was located on the opposite side of the turret, he had to shout instructions to the commander. These tanks were modified in due course, and issued as Stuart Hybrids, mostly to the Far East. In the Mark III, since the turret floor had to clear the shaft altogether, it was at a ridiculous height and the crewmen were squeezed up in their little seats, unable to stand if the hatches were closed down. By May 1943 they made it known that no more of this version were wanted. In fact another new model, the M3A3, or Stuart V was in service by then which was much better. In this version the hull had been entirely redesigned with sloping front and sides that made it much more comfortable; in August 1943 it was learned that production was ending, but a reassurance came from London that sufficient would be available to meet all forseeable British requirements. In reality, by this time, the Stuart was entirely outclassed as a

fighting tank and an interesting field modification was introduced, the so-called Stuart Recce. In Italy this could be any model – the M3, M3A1 or M3A3 – with the turret removed. Although more vulnerable, and virtually toothless except for the odd machine-gun, it proved highly popular. Relieved of both turret and gun it was faster, more mobile and of low silhouette, except when some inventive spirits fitted folding canvas hoods to keep the rain out. As a reconnaissance vehicle it was like a glorified Universal Carrier, yet without that overworked vehicle's frailties. When it wasn't scouting it could be used for casualty evacuation and even as a resupply vehicle, especially for taking quantities of small-arms ammunition to infantry units posted in distant and inaccessible places.

To claim that the Universal Carrier was overworked hardly exaggerates the case. Although it was an anachronism in modern warfare, for it was never either one thing or the other, the Carrier actually increased its versatility and in an effort to meet requirements every opportunity was taken to increase production. In addition to those built in Commonwealth countries for their own use, Canada built large numbers for Britain. Welding was introduced in order to seal the hull for wading, and new examples of the Ford V8 engine were fitted – 85-hp versions, of American, British and Canadian manufacture. All this added to the carrier's weight, which even the more powerful engine failed to counteract, but it retained a reputation for reliability, although frequently compared unfavourably with American four-wheel drive trucks of similar capacity. Its main failings were the shedding of roadwheel tyres and track breakage – overloading aggravated these and also led

16 *The crew of a Stuart V (M3A3) removing a tarpaulin cover in bitter winter conditions. Notice the smoke dischargers on the left of the turret, a typical British modification.*

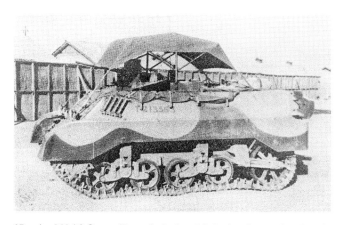

17 *An M3A3 Stuart Recce in Italy with the hood erected and a .50 Browning mounted.*

to engine and gearbox problems. In Italy they were recording an average engine life of 1,000 miles; continual use of intermediate gears caused premature failures in this component.

At the same time a distinct change of role was noticed. The Universal Carrier was becoming precisely what a 1942 War Office document said it was not; an armoured fighting vehicle. The rot set in when it was decided to revert to the use of Vickers machine-guns in motor machine-gun battalions but, in order to improve the field of fire and make easier the task of dismounting the weapon, it was fitted to a pedestal on the Carrier's engine casing. The temptation to fire from the vehicle whenever possible was obvious, as was the urge to carry as much ammunition as there was room for, but it amounted to misuse. Fortunately a similar scheme to mount and fire the 3-inch mortar from the Carrier was abandoned, but the temptation to improve a Carrier's firepower by its crew proved irresistible and before long they were seen sporting surplus Allied or enemy weapons of up to 20-mm calibre, mounted with varying degrees of ingenuity. One commentator refers to attempts to stamp out this practice, which he regarded as leading to an outrageous degree of overloading because the Carrier was expected to carry all sorts of extra stores and ammunition. He was writing from Italy but one wonders what he would have made of a Canadian

18 *A Universal Carrier in the Medium Machine-Gun role, stripped of all its mudguards, possibly to save weight. The unit code number, 64 on a black square, indicates the machine-gun battalion of an infantry division.*

practice noted in North West Europe, which involved the fitting of two banks of PIAT anti-tank projectors – a total of fourteen weapons – to the back of some Carriers, presumably for a lethal Parthian shot if the vehicle was pursued by German armour.

Later experience in both European theatres revealed the vulnerability of Carriers to mines. Their low ground clearance and thin belly-plating meant that such incidents were, inevitably, fatal for the crew, and the natural response was to line the bottom of the hull with sand bags to reduce the risk. This, naturally, compounded the overloading problem and led to a decline in popularity of

these little vehicles which, in most practical respects, had already outlived their usefulness. Even so, as Colonel Gordon-Hall remarked, they were one of the few British armoured vehicles that had entered the war in a complete state of development and he paid them the following tribute, which could not be bettered:

> The Universal Carrier had a long run for its money and, on the whole, paid a good dividend. Its heyday was probably in the Abyssinian campaign where it played a material part in the victory and won golden opinions and, even in the days of its decline, it could still be found turning up gallantly in all sorts of unexpected places, loaded like a Derby Day charabanc but still getting there.

Gordon-Hall's report also mentioned a vehicle that has come to be regarded as the Universal Carrier's poor cousin, the Loyd Carrier. Because it was unarmoured and had two complete suspension units on each side, the Loyd had far better load-carrying potential, although even this was abused. The report explains that many of them, employed in the slave battery role, for which they were not designed, were simply abandoned by regiments who found that they could not even keep up with the tanks which it was their duty to recharge or jump start. Others were adapted as anti-tank gun tractors, and both versions were soon accused of being underpowered, unreliable and prone to overheating. Among other things, suspension units broke, brakes quickly faded and even differential driving axles bent. Gordon-Hall regarded the cooling problem as inherent but claimed that the other problems were due in the main to misuse, pointing out that they were rarely, if ever, used as designed as tracked load

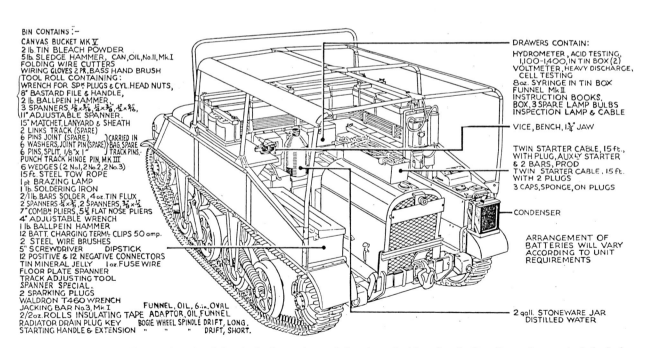

Drawing D: *Stowage diagram for a Loyd Carrier in the starting and charging role. Note that the list of items does not include the heavy tank batteries it would also carry.*

carriers. They rapidly fell out of favour in Italy and were reduced to doing odd jobs.

The difficult nature of the fighting in Italy has been described many times, but it can be simply illustrated with a calendar. By the end of March 1944, after seven months of heavy fighting and two major landings – at Salerno in mid-September 1943 and Anzio in January 1944 – the Allies had still only progressed about half-way up the country, probably less than 400 miles from the toe in a direct line. What a contrast with North Africa. The terrain was a major factor, but it was defended with tenacity and skill, assisted to some extent by the narrow front, and by March the main advance was held up at Cassino, while the forces within the Anzio beach-head were struggling to hold on. Another local feature was highlighted in a report from an unidentified Sherman regiment. This states that in the numerous woods and orchards they would run into German armour and have to fight it out at ranges down to as little as 50 yards. By insisting on careful maintenance of the gun-stabilising gear it was possible to guarantee good shooting on the move and thus gain the advantage, although the report suggests that these conditions were probably peculiar to mountain warfare.

While plans were formulated for a renewed offensive in May, the Churchill tanks began to arrive, the three regiments of 25th Army Tank Brigade late in April, followed by those of 21st Army Tank Brigade fielding what amounted to a new Mark of Churchill, the NA75. During the fighting for Kairouan in Tunisia, forty-eight almost-new Shermans were disabled in a minefield, and as they were recovered for cannibalising and scrapping it was noted that in most cases their 75-mm guns still had about 85 per cent life left in them. It occurred to a REME officer, Captain Percy Morrell, that there was no good reason why these weapons could not be mounted in Churchill tanks and by placing his future military career on the line, against some opposition, he set out to prove it. The type of turret selected was the cast version fitted to the Mark IV, which in any case was by now the standard production model. Following the fighting in Tunisia Churchill crews had pressed hard to have the tanks fitted with a full-width external mantlet. There was a general belief that the shadow created by the internal mantlet made a perfect aiming point for German guns and that such a strike could drive the weapon, mounting and all, back into the turret. In his report, quoted earlier, Colonel Gordon-Hall cast doubt on this, claiming that at normal fighting ranges it was all an enemy gunner could do to draw an accurate bead on a tank, let alone one small part of it, but Morrell, who was working on them constantly, believed that 60 per cent of strikes on Churchills hit this area. Who was right or wrong is not the point: it is what crews believed that matters, since this would affect their confidence, and thus their performance in battle. In any case it was also true that under a sustained attack, even of small arms fire, this area let in bullet splash. Working with

a small but dedicated team Morrell achieved the desired result, but it was a struggle. Measurements had already shown that the American weapons would fit, but it was not simply a matter of cutting a bigger hole in the front of the turret. The interior had to be reshaped – no easy task with a casting – in order to obtain sufficient elevation, and the breech had to be turned through 180 degrees so that the gun could be served from the right, in keeping with the crew layout of a Churchill. The Sherman's periscope gun-sight was arranged to work through a ventilator hole in the Churchill's turret roof, and the elevating gear was modified to suit. The coaxial Browning machine-gun of the Sherman was retained, with some alterations, and to avoid complications with ammunition stowage a Browning was also supplied for the hull gunner's position, in place of the Besa. Firing trials proved the conversion to be effective and a major programme was immediately ordered.

Under the codename 'Whitehot', production began at 16 Base Workshops REME near Bone in Algeria. By June 1944 some 200 Churchill tanks had been converted to what was now known as the Churchill Mark IV (NA75) (NA, of course, for North Africa). As a future chapter will show, 75-mm gun Churchills were also available by this time in Britain, using the British Mark V gun, but with the massive concentration of interest and effort now focused upon the invasion of Europe it is clear that Italy was now regarded by many as a second-class theatre. Certainly the Prime Minister was irritated by the lack of progress, and without his support the chances of getting any new Churchills out there at the expense of the new front in France were slim indeed, so to that extent the NA75 was a godsend, in addition to being a brilliant improvisation. With this in mind it is relevant to comment here on the subject of infantry tank armament, which can also be applied to the new breed of assault tanks then under development. Before the advent of the dual-purpose 75-mm weapon, the practice of equipping tanks designed for infantry support with dedicated anti-tank weapons was regularly called into question, and still is with hindsight. It made good sense, on many counts, to design such tanks around a gun that would be more effective against infantry-style targets such as machine-gun posts or defended buildings, even at the expense of anti-tank performance. In a sense this turned such a tank into a piece of short-range, self-propelled artillery, and it existed in a small way in the Churchill Mark V, which mounted a 95-mm howitzer. However, the current argument was that this was never the true role of an infantry tank. According to the accepted theory, infantry tanks were there not just to help the foot soldiers to their objective, but to protect them, once the objective was gained, from counterattacks by enemy armour. While the only weapons suitable for mounting in tanks were anti-tank guns, this might be seen as a rather disingenuous piece of dogma, but since it never changed while the infantry tank, as a separate class, lasted, one has to accept that there was more to it than that.

19 *A Churchill Mark IV NA75 showing clearly the Sherman gun-mounting fitted to the original turret. The coaxial Browning can be seen, but the hull weapon has not been fitted.*

Following the fall of Cassino, along with the liberation of Rome and the link up with the Anzio enclave, the fighting moved into the Appenines. Here, as already explained, the Churchills came into their own. The neutral turn facility provided by the Merritt-Brown transmission allowed them to negotiate the tightest hairpin bend with ease, while their proven climbing ability got them to locations that very few other tanks could reach. Even so, since there were never enough NA75s to go round six regiments, the squadron composition was changed. Each now comprised two troops of Churchills and two of Shermans plus a squadron HQ troop of Churchills, of which some ultimately had 95-mm howitzers, a total of fifteen tanks in all. Each type had its own role during an attack. The Churchills, having thicker armour, made the initial assault against the main German defences while the Shermans, with their greater speed and 75-mm guns, hung back until a breakthrough had been achieved and then raced through the gap to exploit the enemy's discomfort. All the while they could maintain pressure, the Germans would have difficulty in establishing a new defensive position.

A curious feature of the Churchills, first noted in Tunisia and continued in Italy, was the practice of removing the centre section of the sheet steel trackguard on each side where it flanked the turret. The reason for doing this, according to a report from London, was that this segment could easily be damaged, from enemy fire or contact with obstacles, which would cause it to rise up and jam the turret ring. Since the practice was not observed to anything like the same extent in Europe, it may well have been another of those sincere, but misplaced, beliefs that are honoured for reasons of morale rather than anything else. On the subject of Churchill turrets, another local problem worth recording was a massive increase in the number of cases reported of serious damage to the traversing gear. The cause, it seems, was the vineyards again. They were strung like British hopfields, although in Italy wire was used, and it was strong stuff by all accounts. Tanks moving through the vines would get the wire caught around their guns and turrets until it became drawn so tight that the turret was literally dragged around, ripping out the traversing gear as it went. The problem became so bad that supplies of spares were insufficient to

20   *The Sherman modified in Italy to resist Panzerfaust attack. It is not difficult to see why the wire netting might not have lasted long under active service conditions.*

meet the demand for replacements. On this subject it is worth recording that in Britain, some time earlier, the Admiralty's Department of Miscellaneous Weapon Development once managed to disable a Valentine by entangling it with 600 ft of wire cable originally intended for use against enemy aircraft.

Although in Italy they probably never represented the degree of threat attributed to them in the later fighting in Germany, hand-held anti-tank weapons such as the Panzerfaust were quite unpleasant enough to warrant special consideration. Indeed it is rather surprising to discover that in Italy systems to defeat them were improvised a lot more swiftly than they appear to have been in a theatre that was closer to home. By nature, the Panzerfaust is a weapon of opportunity, fired at short range, with only modest velocity, and relying on the hollow charge principle, initiated by an impact fuse, to penetrate armour. Two methods were devised for dealing with it. One was to fit panels of armour, spaced away from the main body and turret of the tank, which would detonate the projectile but dissipate the effect of the hollow charge before it could do any serious damage. This was the method adopted by the Germans against Allied weapons such as the PIAT or Bazooka. The local British answer was to prevent the fuse from firing by, in effect, catching the projectile in flight and holding it. For experimental purposes a Sherman tank was covered all over with a web of wire netting, loosely held in such a way that it would give when the Panzerfaust

round hit it. It took quite some time to work out the best method of attaching the material to produce just the right effect, and the result looked very untidy indeed. It looked a good deal worse after one or two unexploded Panzerfaust rounds had hit it, but at least under ideal test conditions it appeared to work. In practice, however, it proved absolutely hopeless. After the tank had been driven through a small wood, or a couple of vineyards, there was hardly enough wire netting remaining intact to protect it at all, so the idea was swiftly dropped.

As part of their defence system of the French coast, their Atlantic Wall, the Germans adopted the practice of adding redundant tank turrets, usually of French origin, to the concrete emplacements. They might not be a match for Allied tanks in terms of gun power, but they presented small and difficult targets. In Italy they went one better. Here, at strategic vantage points in later defensive lines, they established dug-in Panther turrets, every bit a match for a Sherman or Churchill. These turrets were of simpler design than genuine Panther tank turrets, but they mounted the same long 75-mm gun and were just as lethal. They were emplaced in such a way that a vital piece of ground – often a road hemmed in at the bottom of a valley – could be covered without having to traverse beyond a limited arc, so that the vulnerable sides of the turret were not unduly exposed. The turret ring formed the top surface of a subterranean box which served as fighting compartment and living quarters for the crew, and a well-sited turret was not easy to spot until it started firing; even then, it was very difficult to knock out. To counter this threat Churchill regiments often worked in conjunction with M10 tank destroyers of the Royal Artillery, an interesting mixture that in some respects came closer to American thinking on the employment of armour. Once they were hit these turrets were easily destroyed, but this could rarely be achieved without sacrificing the first few tanks that got in their way, because they always had the advantage of surprise. For this reason they came to be a particularly dreaded feature of the fighting in Italy.

Many writers have commented on the difficult conditions for tanks in Italy, contrasting them strongly with those in North Africa. One can make the same point with regard to Burma, or North West Europe or even the Russian Front, which seems to beg the question of whether a universal tank really is a valid proposition when considered on a world-wide basis. The Sherman was the only significant tank that fought in all five theatres and it maintained its reputation in every one, but there were sufficient occasions, especially in Italy and Europe, when the Churchill proved far more suitable for certain tasks. A report from Cassino told how Churchill tanks had 'managed to insinuate themselves into the most unlikely places by following obscure tracks in the mountains and it would not be safe for a commander to be too definite when deciding where tanks can or cannot go'. This is not to suggest that a truly universal tank could not have been designed to fulfil all major roles, but it does seem to show that that tank was not the Sherman, no matter what General Montgomery might have believed. Undoubtedly, in the end, the Sherman could have fought its way from one end of Italy to the other without help from the Churchills – the Americans proved that – but it seems fair to assume that it would have taken longer about it and, what is worse, would have cost the lives of many more crews than was otherwise the case.

21 M4A1 (76-mm) gun Shermans of 6th South African Armoured Division near Bologna in 1945.

Although they were fighting against powerful allies, in a country that had turned against them, the German forces in Italy never seem to have suffered from the demoralisation with which they were finally affected in Germany itself. They proved a tough and resourceful enemy to the very end and found valuable, if unwitting allies in the Appenine chain and the fearful winter weather of 1944–5. It took the best part of six months, from August 1944 to March 1945, before their defensive system in the mountains, the Gothic Line, was broken. Towards the end of the campaign British and Commonwealth units were operating improved versions of the Sherman, the British-modified 17-pounder Firefly and the 76-mm gun American model. They were also being assisted by various items of specialised armour.

The subject of specialised armour in the Italian Campaign is an interesting one because it reveals an independence from events at home that was forced upon the participants. Although they had crossed the Mediterranean and were nearer to Britain in a geographical sense, in terms of supply lines British forces in Italy were now further away than ever. Ships carrying new equipment still had to follow the old route out to Egypt, from where it was forwarded to the fighting front in mainland Italy. This accounts for the use of AFVs shipped direct from the United States that were not to be found in North West Europe. In addition, of course, once planning for the Second Front got under way, Italy immediately went on short commons, especially where new tanks and the latest developments in specialised armour were concerned.

Turreted Grant Scorpions of No 1 Scorpion Regiment landed on Sicily during Operation Husky; a well-known photograph of one coming ashore from an LCT (4) gives the lie to a claim that they were too wide to pass through the bows of a normal tank landing craft. Width only became a problem when they tried to cross Bailey bridges. This, however, was a serious problem in Italy, and steps were immediately taken to remedy it. Reports exist of a slimmed-down Grant Scorpion and one is tempted to link this with mention of the Ford V8 engine being replaced by a 30-hp Bedford unit – presumably a straight-six, which would certainly have been thinner than the Ford. Whether or not this was the mysterious Scorpion IV cannot be confirmed, although such a thing existed. This is indicated, not just by the fact that there was a Scorpion V, but also by one lone reference in a War Office report which speaks of the disappointing performance of the Scorpion IV. Other accounts from Italy state that the flail on Scorpions was underpowered, at least when it came to operating in that deep and viscous Italian mud. Whether it was also due to the reduced power output of the Bedford engine compared with the Ford is not explained.

Back in Egypt, in September 1943, both 400 and 401 Independent Squadrons recorded experiments with twin-engined Scorpions. Based at Ikingi Camp, near Amiriya, 400 Squadron claim to have tested one with two Ford V8s and then moved on to a pair of Dodge engines of unspecified type instead. This is what became known as the Scorpion V. The engines, in their armoured housings, partly overhung the tank's engine decks and towered above the turret. A drive shaft from each ran down to opposite ends of the flail rotor, which must have increased the power considerably. Reports printed in London stated that trials in Italy were testing out various types of flail using cable, chain or combinations of both with different forms of head weight. However, the real breakthrough came when the actual arrangement of flails on the rotor drum was changed. The new layout, which had a more continuous beating effect, produced claims of 100 per cent success under trial conditions, which sounds too good to have been true. Having got this far, a sort of perverse pride seems to have overtaken the authorities in Italy towards the end of the war because they became very reluctant to accept Sherman Crab flails when they were offered from Britain, insisting on the superiority of their own design. Yet there was one thing a Crab could do which a Scorpion could not, and that was to cut through barbed wire entanglements. The Italian answer was to fit a pair of Bangalore torpedo explosive demolition tubes beneath the flail arms of a Scorpion. The tank would approach the wire, halt, and then discharge the torpedoes into the wire, where they would remain suspended before exploding and cutting a way through.

Precisely what the Scorpion IV was based on is not clear, but there is no doubt that the Scorpion V was based on a Grant II, an Anglicised version of the Medium M3A5 which had twin General Motors diesels in place of the Wright radial. This was done, presumably, because it was the latest version available, but it does raise the interesting point that here one had a tank which required two kinds of fuel – a potential source of aggravation, if not disaster. The ultimate Middle East pattern Scorpion was applied to a Sherman. It appears to have been the same twin Dodge installation seen on the Grant and may well have retained the same designation, since there is no record of a Scorpion VI. An example is believed to have been shipped back to Britain, but there is no surviving record to show how many were converted, or if they were ever used.

As an approach to mine-clearing the flail was reasonably effective, but it had its limitations. Inequalities in the ground surface could cause the flails to miss a mine, and if a following tank, taking evasive action for any reason, were to swerve off the beaten path it was also likely to come to grief. In order to avoid this, and to allow for the odd tank to become disabled in the cleared area, the normal practice was to have three Scorpions sweeping the minefield in echelon, each tank slightly overlapping the lane of its leader.

The Octopus method was an alternative way of crossing a minefield which gave a lane that was 100 per cent safe for fighting tanks to use, but it could provide only one track, which all had to follow; if there was a breakdown, for

22 A rear, overhead view of the Sherman Scorpion showing the two auxiliary engine mountings. The flail booms and rotor have been stowed for transportation.

23 The original Churchill Octopus at Ottariano, having just run over a mine which has broken the nearside track.

whatever reason, that was that. (Octopus has something in common with Alexander Graham Bell's telephone; it was invented as one thing, but became something else.) The project, which began at Ottariano in Italy, was an exact counterpart of the Sacrificial Tank scheme evolved in the First World War.★

The tank in this case was a redundant Churchill, with its turret removed and long, hinged ramps, in line with the tracks, attached at each end. When a minefield was encountered, a squadron of these Churchills would be brought up, with their ramps erect. At an agreed point the first one would drive into the minefield until it was brought to a halt by striking a mine, which in theory would do little more than break a track and smash up some suspension units. Hopefully the driver would have survived and he would now disengage the ramps, if the blast had not already done so, so that their outer ends fell to the ground. At this point a second Octopus would draw up,

★See D J Fletcher, Landships, HMSO, 1984, p. 38.

following carefully in the tracks of its disabled companion, over which it would climb and then carry on across the field until it, too, struck a mine; and so on, until the other side of the danger zone had been reached. Now one would have a causeway, or at least a series of stepping stones, bridging the minefield from side to side, across which the fighting tanks could proceed in safety. There were so many potential disasters in such an arrangement that it is difficult to spot the advantages. It was extravagant in tanks, even if they were older Churchills fit for little else, and they would be difficult to recover and repair. Then there was the risk to the driver and any other crew member, although this could be minimised by adding extra internal armour. Finally there were the difficulties faced by the fighting tanks that had to cross the minefield in this way. It takes a great deal of skill to line a tank up on a pair of narrow ramps scarcely wider than the tank itself. Enemy fire is apt to make concentration difficult and under such conditions the driver will be closed down, with a limited view and obviously without external guidance. If the minefield is deep a tank might have to go through this evolution two or three times in succession, alternately exposing its vulnerable underside or top plates on each ramp and at other times rising nearly six feet above the surrounding battlefield as a very prominent target. Any tank knocked out during this operation would effectively render the entire causeway useless; and just imagine being trapped, under fire, in a Churchill Octopus with a burning Sherman sitting on top. A turretless Sherman with similar ramps was developed in Italy and also named Octopus, so

it may have been part of the same project. However, the shape of a Sherman's hull does not lend itself to this kind of use and it appears to have been dropped at the experimental stage. So was the Churchill, as far as minefield crossing was concerned, but it was diverted to another purpose.

The sequence of fortified lines built across Italy by the Germans included some deep anti-tank ditches, and in certain parts of the country there were natural obstacles equally capable of arresting a tank. The Octopus tanks were therefore allocated to a new role as ditch fillers. When an obstacle was identified, one of the tanks would drive up and insert itself into the gap, dropping its ramps to allow other AFVs to cross over on its back. In this form it was rechristened ARK, because the flat deck gave it the appearance of an aircraft carrier, among which *HMS Ark Royal* was probably the best known. At least twenty-five were built for service in Italy, distinguished from the British-made version by having no decking above the vehicle's tracks. Thus a tank using the ARK made direct contact track-to-track, although this does not appear to have done them any harm. ARKs were probably used more extensively in Italy than anywhere, and certainly more dramatically. A deep ditch near the River Senio required two, one on top of the other, to fill it, while in order to cross the River Savio a causeway of six or more was required, although this use was open to the same objections as a minefield causeway and there are reports of one or more drivers having been drowned getting them into position.

24 *The Sherman Octopus under test at MEE Italy. A Churchill Mark VII is crossing, putting an unbelieveable strain on the Sherman's suspension.*

25 *The spectacular mobile Brown Bailey bridge, seen from the pusher tank end.*

When larger gaps had to be tackled the British Army employed the Bailey bridge, a prefabricated structure which was transported by lorries and erected on site. Obviously when this had to be done under fire casualties could be expected, and in the tradition of their Corps the Royal Engineers accepted this. All the same, if life-saving alternatives could be found there was no sense in ignoring them. Once again the solution had already been developed at the end of the First World War and it was basically a matter of adapting it to current equipment. The original military bridge was the Inglis, and it was still in use early in the Second World War when trials were carried out in conjunction with a Matilda tank which pushed it into place. The Bailey bridge being that much more substantial, greater power was needed to shift it, and various expedients were developed. Once in Italy, as an emergency measure, a Bailey bridge had been launched at night using Caterpillar bulldozers and this had resulted in the development of special skids on which the assembled bridge rested. In order to help steer it, a pilot tank was attached to the front of the bridge while another pushed from the back; about one hundred feet short of the gap the leading tank disengaged, while the other pushed the bridge in place. By this arrangement a gap of up to 60 feet could be bridged. Skid Baileys, as they were called, were employed in North West Europe.

Slightly more sophisticated was the Mobile Bailey, where a 160-foot section of bridge rested on a set of dumb tracks located just ahead of the point of balance. This was designed to deal with a 70-foot gap; the extra length was needed to fulfil the launching process. When the leading end of the bridge was hovering over the far bank, the tracked undercarriage would still be on the nearside. The tank would then disengage and, by means of ramps, climb on to the nearer end of the bridge. This would effectively break the upper chord of the bridge somewhere near its mid-point, causing the opposite end to drop in place.

Finally, with the Brown and Dalton bridges things were taken to their logical conclusion. This system used two tanks: a Churchill to push, and a turretless one, or ARK, to support the bridge. The carrier tank had rollers on its upper surface, and the idea was that it halted on the bank while the pusher continued to shove the bridge over it until the gap had been bridged. Both tanks then reversed clear.

Valentine scissors bridgelayers were employed in Italy, where they were adapted to take a No 19 wireless set. This proved so successful that the Department of Tank Design initiated a scheme to modify those in Britain along the same lines. Valentines with anti-mine rollers fitted were still operating with Scorpion flail regiments, and a roller device was also adapted to fit the Staghound armoured car, although there is no evidence of it ever being used. In fact where mines were concerned the Staghound had become something of a favourite, due to its ability to survive them. In any place where their presence was suspected, arrangements would be made in an armoured car regiment to have a Staghound lead the way. Even an anti-tank mine would do little more than blow off one of the front wheels: the crew were rarely harmed and on at least one occasion continued to fight from the stationary car without any difficulty. Another development from this theatre for which no convincing explanation has yet been found is a turretless M10 tank destroyer with an enormous V-shaped snow plough attached to the front. It may well have been intended for snow clearance but it was actually demonstrated on soil. If, as has been suggested, it was intended to unearth mines, one feels sorry for the operator. He was stationed on the glacis plate of the tank, within the V of the plough, behind an enormous handwheel which raised or lowered it. Assuming such a position to have been untenable under fire, it would be dangerous enough in peaceful conditions. Although a plough is intended to unearth mines without detonating them, there is always the risk of one going off, and a mine struck by the very apex of the plough would certainly explode, with the added risk of the blast penetrating beneath the blade, just where the operator was sitting.

26 *The turretless M10 plough on test in Italy. The vulnerable control position for the blade is clearly shown.*

The Sherman bulldozer was a much more popular device. This was an American conversion, easily applied to most types of Sherman. The blade was of the flat, full width type, attached by trunnions to a bracket that connected the tank's two leading suspension units. A simple hydraulic device on the nose of the tank, operated by the driver, lifted the blade clear of the road for driving, and in every other respect the tank remained in full fighting trim. Although it was quite late in the war before British units received any, they were immediately popular, especially in Italy. In Britain, for some reason, it was found necessary to introduce a further modification, although whether one could call it an improvement is debatable. This adaption was called the 'travelling hoist', and it consisted of a system of wire ropes and pulleys attached respectively to the blade and the tank. When not required for bulldozing, cables from the blade ran over pulleys on the hull sides to clamps fitted to the top run of the tracks. The tank then reversed slowly and the tracks, pulling on the cables, hauled the bulldozer arms into an upright position so that the blade was suspended horizontally above the turret like some enormous, rectangular

27 An M4A4 (Sherman V) fitted with the American M1 Dozer attachment and British Travelling Hoist device. The blade is clamped in the upright position.

umbrella. Here it was secured by catches on the hull top, the cables were removed from the tracks, and the tank was ready to go. By May 1945 when the war in Europe ended, 156 had been produced for the British Army out of an order for 309. A contemporary report described this as a British conversion, although everything except the hoist was standard American M1 equipment. How popular this adaption was is another matter. It certainly did nothing to conceal the tank and, if a catch failed or was shot away with the blade in the travelling position, the resulting crash would have been devastating to anyone within earshot, if it did no worse damage to the equipment.

Towards the end of the war the entire panoply of specialised armour began to appear in Italy. Most will be discussed in greater detail elsewhere, but it should be noted that only a few saw active service. These included Valentine and Sherman DD tanks which, along with American LVTs, took part in some amphibious operations towards the end of the war, and locally built versions of the Kangaroo personnel carrier converted from Shermans and Priest self-propelled guns. Sherman Kangaroos were used to lift 2/6th Battalion, the Queen's during Operation Cygnet, an attack against the remaining German pocket south of the River Senio early in January 1945. The Kangaroos were manned by 4th Hussars supported by Shermans of 10th Hussars and 2nd RTR, along with Cabrank bombing by the RAF. Despite unpromising conditions the operation was a great success, although it was remarked afterwards that the Kangaroos should never operate without some tanks in close support, since they had no offensive power of their own. Another local modification used during Cygnet was the Sherman fascine carrier. Like the Kangaroo it was a 'sawn-off' or turretless tank, but in this case fitted with launcher rails above the turret ring. Here the fascines were carried, and dropped by a quick release gear. On this occasion the tank was also used to carry reserve stocks of ammunition for the fighting tanks, but when it was called upon to provide some for B Squadron, 2nd RTR it proved difficult to lift the stuff out from underneath the fascines.

28 A Sherman II (M4A1) fascine carrier followed by an M4A4 Sherman dozer without the Travelling Hoist attachment.

3 The next generation

It is impossible to divide the War neatly in two, and in order to assess tank development in the second half it is first necessary to go back to 1940. By July of that year, even while work was progressing on the Covenanter and Crusader, consideration was being given to what should follow. Any new tank would of course be designed around the 6-pounder gun, although the horrendous triple combination of 2-pounder, 3-inch howitzer and Besa machine-gun was still an option. Initially the choice lay between a specification drawn up by the Directorate of Tanks and Transport or a design offered by the Special Vehicle Development Committee, Sir Albert Stern's 'Old Gang'.

Despite high-pressure lobbying by Stern and his team the former was preferred, and it broke down into three possibilities. General Staff specification A23 was a design by Vauxhall Motors for a cruiser version of the Churchill, with 75-mm frontal armour of riveted or welded construction, powered by the Bedford twelve-cylinder engine driving through a five-speed gearbox and Merritt-Brown transmission. The tank would have a crew of five, A22-style protected suspension, and access doors in the hull sides. Nuffield Mechanisation and Aero offered A24, based on their Crusader with a new turret to carry the 6-pounder. On 25 November 1940 a preliminary design for this tank was submitted, in conjunction with the Department of Tank Design. The specification called for a tank with between 63.5 mm and 75 mm of frontal armour, a 60-inch turret ring (against 54 inches on the Crusader) and an escape hatch in the turret rear. The 6-pounder or triple mount could be fitted, while the General Staff also wanted a series of protected loopholes around the turret through which a Thompson sub-machine-gun could be fired. The crew remained at five, the suspension Christie and the engine a 410-hp V12, clearly an uprated Liberty, with a four-speed gearbox and Wilson, or other approved type of steering system. The designers were aiming for a top speed of 24 mph. The third offering came from the Birmingham Railway Carriage and Wagon Company and was described as a heavy cruiser which differed from Crusader in respect of suspension and tracks, as well as being an estimated half-ton lighter than A24. In fact, except for the suspension of A23, all three tanks looked very much the same, as one might expect since they had to conform with DTD requirements.

The proposed tanks, initially styled Heavy Cruisers, were considered at a Tank Board meeting presided over by the Minister of Supply on 17 January 1941, where it was stressed that the new tank must be in production by the spring of 1942. For this reason it was essential to base the design closely on existing types in order to avoid the need for prototypes; the short-cut route to disaster was still favoured. Geoffrey Burton protested that prototypes and pilot models were essential in every case, but this plea fell on unreceptive ears. Initially a decision was reached in favour of the Nuffield design, six tanks being ordered from Mechanisation and Aero on 29 January 1941, which presumably could be considered as pilot models; some notice was taken of the BRC&W design, but the Vauxhall Motors offering was rejected.

Meanwhile, events were taking place away from the Tank Board and the accepted circle of tank and component producers, which were to have a profound effect on British tank design; they had their beginnings in the Rolls-Royce plant at Derby. In accordance with plans laid down before the war, Rolls-Royce had turned over their entire production to Merlin V12 aircraft engines which had been required immediately for Spitfire, Hurricane and Defiant fighters and Lancaster bombers, among others. At first there was such demand that little time or space had been available for the development of new aero engines, while any further work on luxury private cars was clearly out of the question. Thus the firm was left supporting a team of gifted design engineers under the executive lead of W A (Roy) Robotham with nothing to do. Robotham located the disused and dilapidated Clan Foundry near Belper where he stored some prototype cars and, with characteristic optimism, completed design work for the eventual post-war car programme. Looking for more warlike work, this team then completed the design of a 40-mm gun, but was still seriously under-employed. In October 1940 Robotham met an old schoolfriend, Henry Spurrier, who was general manager of his family's business, Leyland Motors. Leylands were then engaged in tank production – building engines for the Matilda and in due course complete tanks such as A13 and Covenanter. Spurrier was therefore well placed to appreciate some of the problems that afflicted British tank design, and in particular he was concerned at the relatively low horse-power rating of their engines. This was something that Robotham had the necessary expertise to deal with, and having gained the approval of his chief, Walter Hives, he set the Clan Foundry team to work.

Since priority was then being given to the cruiser tank programme, it was clear that whatever engine they developed it would have to fit into the same sort of space previously allotted to the Liberty. Furthermore they would be working with high-powered aircraft engines which would require intensive cooling if they were to perform under armour, putting even greater pressure on the available space. Lacking any kind of tank experience Robotham added three Leyland engineers to his team and began by looking at available engines in the Rolls-Royce inventory. These were narrowed down to a pair of 60-degree V12s, the Kestrel and Merlin. The former had the advantages of being smaller, and already available in unsupercharged form, but it was reckoned that on lower-quality service petrol it could not be expected to develop more than 475 hp, which was hardly much of an improvement on the Liberty. Thus the Mark III variant of the Merlin was selected, and in a remarkably short time an unsupercharged model had been produced with dry-sump lubrication, dual twin-choke carburettors and an effective fan-drive system, which was christened the Meteor. The next problem was to fit it into a tank.

The obvious test bed was a Crusader, but coming from outside the system, indeed even outside the Ministry of Supply, except for the tenuous link through Leylands, Robotham found great difficulty in gathering information. He remarks in his autobiography,[*] in connection with the secrecy surrounding Crusader, that if Hitler could have been persuaded to go into production with the tank, as it then existed, it would have been the most successful sabotage operation of the century! On the test bench at Leylands the modified engine delivered 600 hp, and on 6 April 1941 the first Meteor-engined Crusader was dispatched to Aldershot for preliminary trials. The story of that first test run has been told before;[†] suffice it to say that the performance of the tank exceeded all expectations – the time-keepers were so astonished they forgot to flag the tank as it passed their check-points, while the driver failed to take a corner at the end of the run and plunged into a wood. Without accurate timing the top speed could only be estimated from the revolution-counter readings, which suggested something in the region of 50 mph. Further tests included an attack on the 1 in 2.43 Miles Hill, part of the Farnborough training circuit, which the Meteor-engined Crusader sailed up while three others, all equipped with the Liberty, failed. The Department of Tank Design described this as a 'most attractive performance'. Yet shortly afterwards Leylands announced that they had lost faith in the project, and asked the Ministry of Supply to release them from a contract for over a thousand Meteors in favour of the Liberty.

The main reason given by Leylands for this amazing reversal of policy was concern about cooling. Possibly taking their cue from other pessimistic engineers regarded as experts, they became convinced that any modified aircraft engine of such power could never be successfully cooled within the confines of a tank's hull. Yet trials revealed that, expressed as a proportion of the total power output, the Meteor used up 5 per cent of its available horsepower while the equivalent figure for a Liberty was

17.5 per cent. If Leyland's attitude is difficult to fathom, it must be considered against that of the Ministry of Supply which allowed them to do it. The result on British tank production would soon be evident, but in the meantime it was vital to find an alternative source for Meteors. Robotham took the problem to Hives, already up to his eyes on work with the Merlin, and he in turn presented it as a purely financial problem to Lord Beaverbrook. The result is summed up in the words of the Beaver's well-known telegram; 'OHMS MINISTRY OF SUPPLY TO W. HIVES ROLLS ROYCE NIGHTINGALE ROAD DERBY THE BRITISH GOVERNMENT HAS GIVEN YOU AN OPEN CREDIT OF ONE MILLION POUNDS STOP THIS IS A CERTIFICATE OF CHARACTER AND REPUTATION WITHOUT PRECEDENT OR EQUAL STOP ** BEAVERBROOK **'. Shortly afterwards, Rolls-Royce accepted their first contract for 1,000 Meteor engines.

Robotham's work on the Meteor soon brought him into contact with other industrial concerns involved in tank production and, as an executive of a firm devoted to perfection, he became increasingly irritated. Whether he expressed his views strongly or not is impossible to confirm, but in November 1941 he was appointed to a newly created post within the Ministry of Supply under Oliver Lucas as Chief Engineer of Tank Design, which must have gone down well with engineers who had been in the business for years. In fact the new post had originally been offered to Harry Ainsworth, the Briton who was general manager of Hotchkiss et Cie in France. As recorded in the previous volume,[‡] Ainsworth was by then in the United States and he was apparently selected without any sort of interview, which was described by Colonel W M Blagden as 'a typical instance of the airy manner in which wizards of commerce sometimes approach the problems of running a Government Department'. Three days after receiving his contract Ainsworth was sacked by Lord Beaverbrook. The idea that anyone could design tanks was still strong; this is not to denigrate Robotham's engineering skills, less still his exceptional talent as an executive, but it does seem ridiculous, at a time of national crisis, to have filled such a significant post with a novice, not only as an engineer of armoured vehicles but in all matters concerning tank warfare as well. Robotham subsequently became a member of the Tank Board and the principal result of his involvement, apart from the Meteor engine, was the A30 Challenger tank.

At a Tank Board meeting in December 1941 it was announced that the first Mechanisation and Aero cruiser, now known as the Cromwell, would go down to Lulworth for gunnery trials as soon as the turret was ready. Production

---

*W A Robotham, *Silver Ghosts and Silver Dawn*, Constable, 1970.
†Anon, *Cromwell Tank*, HMSO, 1983, p x.

‡D J Fletcher, *The Great Tank Scandal*, HMSO, 1989, p 88.

was to be shared between the parent company and Ruston and Hornsby of Lincoln, but it was already well behind schedule. A report submitted in the previous August claimed that the delay was due to interference from the Naval Land Equipment (NELLIE) programme and emergency work to mount a 6-pounder gun in the Crusader turret. A pilot Cromwell arrived for trials at Farnborough on 19 March 1942, and was reckoned to be four months late. Initial trials revealed faults in the cooling system, fan-drive and engine bearings, all of which it seems to have inherited from the Crusader, but when it was resubmitted some time later there was a major engine failure and the report concluded with the view that the tank was not yet satisfactory. In fact by this time the Cromwell I, as it was now being called, had already been eclipsed, and was doomed to extinction.

The only obvious alternative was the Birmingham Railway Carriage and Wagon Company heavy cruiser. Robotham had met Harry Moyses, managing director of hat company, in the early stages of the Meteor development and had interested him in the new engine, but a question mark still hung over the transmission. Inspired by their success with the engine, Rolls-Royce and Leyland between them had developed a new unit combining a five-speed synchromesh gearbox with controlled differential steering, while the Tank Board preferred the Merritt-Brown system, despite its teething troubles in the Churchill. Nuffields, of course, would have nothing to do with either of them. Robotham says that the degree of technical skill available on the shop floor at BRC&W was remarkable, enabling them to manufacture prototype parts in record time; the result was that the first prototype of a Meteor-engined heavy cruiser was running at the works on 20 January 1942, two months ahead of the Nuffield A24.

29 *The A27M Cromwell prototype showing the large bolts securing the turret armour. The hull machine-gun mounting has not been fitted.*

Even so, the defection of Leylands from Meteor production was disastrous. The projected cruiser programme for 1942–3 called for 3,700 tanks, and by this time the Nuffield input was virtually written off. As early as 19 September 1941 it had been discovered that it was impossible to standardise their design with the BRC&W machine, and reading between the lines, especially in the light of what comes later, one is forced to the conclusion that Lord Nuffield meant to keep it that way. By intuition and great strength of character this unconventional autocrat had built a vast industrial empire, and while there is no doubting his sincerity and patriotism, it is easy to believe that he would adhere to his own course and contract, no matter what experts from other firms might tell him, or Government ministers demand. On the day that the Meteor-powered cruiser first ran at BRC&W, the order for Nuffield's version was reduced to 500 tanks. All that remained was to sort out Leylands.

The course chosen was an intelligent one under the circumstances, always accepting that such circumstances had been allowed to arise in the first place. This was to have Leylands build the BRC&W cruiser in slightly modified form to accept the Liberty engine and to make similar modifications to the original BRC&W model so that, in theory, either tank could take either engine. What makes the decision such a pitiable one is a report from Farnborough following trials of the Meteor cruiser over February and March 1942. The words used are 'exceptionally good'; when had these words last been heard of a British-built tank? That this was anticipated is clear from a statement issued in January 1942 when the General Staff announced that the new tank was so much better than the Nuffield product that they were prepared to wait longer for it, and would continue building obsolete models in the mean time. An early statement that the BRC&W tank was different in respect of suspension and tracks from the Crusader should not be taken too literally. In fact the suspension was still Christie, fitted with strengthened axle arms and better provided with shock absorbers. To the untrained eye the three new heavy cruisers were almost identical, and all mounted virtually the same turret. Such difference as there was is recognised in a new General Staff specification; Nuffield's A24, or Cromwell I, was now joined by the Leyland A27L (for Liberty) (otherwise the Cromwell II), and BRC&W's A27M (Meteor), the Cromwell III. This recipe for confusion was not sorted out until about November 1942 when A24 became Cavalier, A27L Centaur, while A27M remained simply Cromwell, and these names will be used in all future references. The first Centaur was running at Leylands by July 1942, but subsequent trials revealed that its Liberty engine had a shorter life expectancy than a similar unit in a Crusader, which in itself was not saying much. If all this talk of new cruiser tanks should appear to suggest that the older ones had been forgotten it is worth recording that the production run of Crusaders by the Nuffield Group was not

30 *Rear view of an early A27L Centaur fitted with a long-range fuel tank.*

scheduled to end until September 1943 and that the building of Cavaliers would run concurrently. Once this programme was complete the arrangements were that they should switch to Centaur production under the parentage of Leyland Motors – a step that clearly did not suit Lord Nuffield at all. In February 1943 he caused one of his senior executives, Sir Miles Thomas, to approach the AFV Division of the Ministry with a suggestion which, in retrospect, seems little short of outrageous. This was that the Nuffield Group should continue to build Cavalier in lieu of Centaur. Sir Miles submitted eight points in which, in his view, Cavalier outshone Centaur. Four only are worthy of comment, the others being of too detailed a nature even to warrant consideration. These four were:

1. Superior floorplate design.
2. A tried suspension embodying experience of the Crusader.
3. Superior wheel hubs.
4. Use of a well-tried gearbox and steering system which was lighter than the Merritt-Brown.

Items 1 and 3 were dismissed, as were the other four, by the AFV Division on the basis that Centaur would evolve and improve anyway, but items 2 and 4 seem positively breathtaking. That anyone, in 1943, should have attempted even to mention the Crusader with the intention of boosting Cavalier must have seemed the height of deluded optimism. In any case, as the Tank Board minutes recorded, Cavalier's suspension was already on limit whereas Centaur could expect to improve along the lines of the Cromwell.

Since they were so similar, a general description will suffice for all, and that only as a supplement to the photographs. The hull, which was of riveted construction, was low and flat, with the suspension units sandwiched between inner and outer side plates as on the Crusader. The stepped front had been introduced in order to provide a location for a hull machine-gun, in a similar way to the

31 *The Cavalier as it never was. A drawing by the* Illustrated London News *artist Bryan de Grineau which graced the original vehicle handbook.*

32 *WRAC personnel servicing an A24 Cavalier. From this angle the Crusader-style rear hull, which identifies it from the A27, is clearly shown.*

Churchill, and no use whatever was made of sloped armour. The turret indeed was little more than a flat-faced box, formed from a welded substructure to the vertical faces of which thick armour panels were bolted from the inside, using huge, cone-shaped bosses in place of nuts. The rear turret escape hatch originally specified in the Nuffield contract was eliminated, while a pistol port on each side replaced the suggested tommy-gun ports.

The gun-mounting was similar to that of the Churchill, with the same internal mantlet that was supposed to make crews nervous on account of the shadow it cast, but although power traverse was employed the 6-pounder gun was still only elevated by free movement of a shoulder piece, there being no gearing, manual or otherwise. It is important that we should remember, when the design of these tanks is being discussed, that they were based on a general scheme which had beeen drawn up towards the end of 1940 when the desert war was in its infancy. If this is not appreciated then one finds oneself wondering why certain archaic features were still being incorporated in

1942, although it fails to explain why more adjustments were not made to the design as a result of subsequent experience. Free elevation of the main armament is a good example. It will be recalled that the reason for adopting this method in the first place had to do with the preferred British practice of firing on the move. The technique had been worked out at Lulworth between the wars, although the Medium tanks then in service had employed manual geared elevation and traverse,* but by 1939 it could be described as Royal Armoured Corps dogma. Faster tanks with more flexible suspensions rendered geared elevation ineffective and the gunner in a British cruiser handled his main weapon almost like a glorified rifle. In a fast-moving mêlée at close range this was fine, but as ranges increased in the desert it became more difficult to draw an accurate bead on a small target from a moving tank, and even when firing stationary, from a hull-down position, for instance, a weapon with geared elevation would probably have given more consistent results, except in the hands of an ace gunner. In any case, the 6-pounder was a much heavier piece than the 2-pounder, so it was even more important that the gun should be well-balanced. This in turn meant that a good deal more of the weapon would be inside the turret, and that restricted the available space.

33 *The Vauxhall Cromwell prototype showing the cast/welded turret design.*

When their A23 Cruiser design was rejected in favour of Cromwell, Vauxhall Motors found themselves in a bit of a quandary. Agreement had already been reached that Churchill production would cease and, once the rework programme was complete, they stood a chance of losing their significant place in Britain's tank programme. The Ministry of Supply required them to join the A27M cruiser team but, in keeping with their usual deference, permitted Vauxhall's engineers to modify the design to suit their own production techniques. The most obvious result of this leniency was a new turret design, following the approximate outline of the existing one but of novel construction. Details of this will be found later in this chapter when the new Churchill Mark VII is discussed. For reasons that will be explained, it never passed beyond this prototype stage.

A position had now been reached at which the War Office could gaze with some confidence into the future. By 1943 their short-term tank policy was at least starting to take shape and the General Staff had even managed to focus on long-term plans to develop a universal tank. For the short term, the foreseeable future, Cromwell looked set to become a reliable cruiser, and even the much-abused Churchill showed signs of developing into a serviceable infantry tank. There would be difficulties and mistakes ahead, plenty of them, but in a sense the worst was over and the future could only be better. In any case there was a safety net. Production of Shermans in the United States was gathering pace and the tank was popular with British crews for its reliability and versatile gun. This was the next British problem, to find a better gun.

It already existed, at least theoretically, in the form of the 17-pounder, and its installation in a tank had been discussed by the Tank Board as early as 9 December 1941. Unfortunately at that time the only British tank with a turret ring capable of mounting it was the 80-ton TOG 2, and even the Tank Board baulked at that. In any case the Eighth Army, then the embodiment of all combat experience and wisdom as far as Britain was concerned, was not asking that all tanks should carry a 17-pounder. In their view, the ideal weapon was a dual-purpose 75-mm gun or similar, mounted in a moderately armoured, highly mobile tank. Only a proportion, about 25 per cent, of 17-pounder tanks would be required to support these, for a role that was described in some reports as 'hole punching'. It only remained for the General Staff to pronounce upon the matter, which they did, in a reported dated 23 December 1942. In essence, for the short-term tank programme, they required 'A first-class anti-tank weapon of the 6-pounder type or heavier, modernised to its highest performance, which could outclass enemy tanks of corresponding type; in addition it should be an efficient weapon against personnel and lorries'. They regarded the American 75-mm as the best dual-purpose weapon yet produced, pointing to the advantages of standardisation, and implied that they would be happy to see it adopted as main armament for the majority of British tanks, even if this meant building a version of the Sherman in Britain! Nothing more is heard of this heretical idea, at least on this side of the Atlantic. Meanwhile the War Office asked if a suitable gun with adequate high-explosive performance would be supplied in 1943, pointing out that they would be satisfied with a performance equal to that of the Sherman's 75-mm. It was really a matter of what else was available.

Three new British tank guns were under development in 1942. One had been developed by the Royal Arsenal and was known as the 8-pounder. Little is known about it, and some of the information that does survive conflicts.

*D J Fletcher, *Mechanised Force*, HMSO, 1991, p 9.

One source claims that it was of the same calibre (57-mm) as the 6-pounder and that it would fit into the 6-pounder cradle, while another gives the calibre as 60-mm and says that it would not fit. Both sources agree that designs were prepared for long- and short-barrelled versions and that, irrespective of the cradle, the longer gun could not be accommodated in any existing British turret. It is also claimed that the anti-tank performance of the shorter version – the only one that could be used – was no better than the longer version of the 6-pounder, so that was clearly going nowhere. Worse still, it was discovered that the longer round supplied for this gun would not fit into British turrets either, so that was the end of the 8-pounder.

Vickers, meanwhile, had developed a 12-pounder (70-mm) tank gun. This would fit in place of a 6-pounder, and so would the ammunition, but its armour-piercing performance was described as being not appreciably superior to the 6-pounder, and its high-explosive potential, while better than that of the 6-pounder, did not match up to the American 75-mm. Vickers managed to install a 12-pounder into a Valentine and undertake successful firing trials, but by that time another new gun was in the offing, from the same stable. This was a high-velocity, 75-mm weapon with a barrel length of 50 calibres. It was discussed in March 1942, when it was stated that it appeared practicable to fit it into the Cromwell turret, but fourteen months later, just as prototypes were ordered, the awful truth dawned.

Clearly there had always been some doubt about the chances of fitting the new, high-velocity 75-mm into the Cromwell, at least without major modifications, because discussion ran on through the summer and autumn of 1942. Woven in with it was a suggestion, the merest hint, that a 75-mm which might fit into the 6-pounder mounting would be ideal. It seems to have been enough, despite the on-and-off interest, since by Christmas all was revealed. The first mention one finds of this is in that same report, from the Adelphi, dated 23 December 1942. General Weeks, the chairman, explained that Vickers-Armstrong had produced an outline design for converting the 6-pounder to take American 75-mm ammunition. Naturally this gun was bound to fit into the 6-pounder mounting. It seems such a simple solution that one wonders, as one always does when faced with the blindingly obvious, why nobody had thought of it before – after all, the 6-pounder was not even a Vickers-Armstrong weapon. General Weeks went on to say that drawings of the American 75-mm would be supplied to Vickers to enable them to finalise the design, and the Director General of Weapons Production would rapidly produce a number of guns for experimental purposes, while some tanks would be made available in which the stowage arrangements could be worked out. Speed was naturally of the essence and this was helped by the fact that the ammunition, and consequently the internal ballistics, of

the gun would be the same as for the American weapon, so performance trials would not be necessary. All that was required was to test the recoil mechanism and carry out standard user trials. Indeed there was only one drawback. The performance of the gun was such that geared elevation would be essential, and since the weapon was intended primarily for Cromwell, something would have to be developed. At that time, it was pointed out, the only British tank in service with geared elevation was the Valentine.

Another outcome of this meeting is worth a passing comment. This was a report to the effect that the 17-pounder gun could be adapted to fire 3.7-inch high-explosive and armour-piercing high-explosive (APHE) ammunition. Presumably this was an attempt to make this gun into a dual-purpose weapon as well, but it had more drawbacks. In the first place the weight of the piece would increase by 4 cwt. Secondly the recoil energy would be very high, so that an extremely efficient muzzle brake would be required, but it was calculated that, firing APHE, the new gun would only be slightly inferior, as an armour-piercing weapon, to the standard 17-pounder. Meanwhile, Vickers-Armstrong continued design work on their new, high-velocity 75-mm gun with its barrel length of 50 calibres – compared with the 36.5 calibres of the medium-velocity piece developed from the 6-pounder. A meeting of the AFV Liaison Committee on 2 March 1943 was given to understand that the new gun could be fitted to Cromwell and, on the strength of that, six prototype weapons were ordered on 13 April. Design progress was good and it was confidently anticipated that production would start in the second quarter of 1944 when, at a meeting held on 25 May 1943, the Committee learned that it was not possible to fit the gun into a Cromwell turret after all: the turret ring was too small. There was a minor explosion from the General Staff, with the suggestion that the Ministry of Supply had held back this bad news on purpose. If production of the gun was to proceed it would be necessary to design a new tank for it. The result will be explained in the final chapter. The last, and sourest, note came from the Director General of Artillery, Major-General Sir Campbell Clarke. His view was that the requirements for high armour-piercing performance and high-explosive performance against ground targets were incompatible, and that the proposal by Vickers to make a medium-velocity 75-mm out of the 6-pounder was an unsatisfactory compromise.

While efforts were being made to produce an adequate dual-purpose weapon, the original concept of a separate close support tank was still being pursued. It drew, of course, on similar experience in the desert and consequently required a weapon which had a good high-explosive performance in preference to the previous preoccupation with firing smoke shells. The new piece, which became known as the 95-mm howitzer, was developed in 1942 by fitting a cut-down 3.7 inch gun barrel with a 25-pounder breech assembly. In this form it was capable of firing a 25-pounder round over a maximum effective range of 5,000 yards. Naturally it was intended that it should fit into the 6-pounder mounting, and the original scheme was to use the two-man (6-pounder) Crusader turret, a proportion of which would be produced as close support tanks. Unfortunately, preliminary tests revealed that in this mounting the gun was limited to a range of 2,500 yards. Whether this was due to restricted elevation, or stress on the mounting from a full charge, is not revealed, but it clearly annoyed the Director of Armoured Fighting Vehicles who said that he had been promised 5,000 yards, and was not prepared to accept half.

Since the new 75-mm gun was interchangeable with the 6-pounder it followed that it could be installed in any armoured fighting vehicle designed to accept the latter weapon. Consequently when a requirement was identified for a 75-mm gun armoured car the obvious step was to convert the AEC Mark II. This was reported in the Middle East in August 1943, just as a pilot vehicle was undergoing initial trials at Lulworth. These revealed that with the new weapon there was a greater build-up of fumes within the turret, so the number of electric extractor fans mounted in the turret roof was increased from one to two. With the design settled it was agreed to complete the last 200 cars with the new weapon; these were styled as the AEC Mark III. The same requirement also affected the Coventry armoured car, already mentioned in Chapter 1.

A combined Daimler and Rootes group effort, the Coventry (or AFVW19 as it was officially designated) was a rare attempt in wartime Britain to produce a standardised design for an armoured car which, experience might have suggested, was doomed from the outset. It had a well-shaped hull with a rear-mounted Hercules six-cylinder engine and a turret which looked like a squat version of the type fitted to the Daimler. The 2-pounder

gun was specified at first, although an idea put forward in September 1942 to fit surplus 2-pounder turrets from early Churchill tanks might have led to premature disaster and a really ugly armoured car. Maximum armour thickness was quoted as 14-mm, even less than the Daimler, yet the total weight at 11.5 tons was only about a ton less than an AEC, which had twice the armour thickness and a 75-mm gun. An order for 1,700 Coventrys was placed in 1943 with the comment that it should be possible to mount the 6-pounder gun, although the two prototypes delivered by Daimler and Humber mounted the 2-pounder. Having studied the specifications, the Eighth Army remarked in May 1943 'we are beginning to feel serious doubt as to whether the Coventry is not already out of date', while the trials report published by Lulworth a few months later revealed a low standard of fighting efficiency due to the layout of the fighting compartment. Another report explained one reason why the car was so heavy: each wheel weighed about 700 pounds, thus accounting for 1¼ tons of the total weight. Fuel and oil consumption was also 'somewhat high'. At about the same time, a 75-mm version was proposed with the official designation AFVW90. One of the original pilots was rebuilt to this configuration and 900 were ordered. It demanded a larger turret with a flat frontal face and a reduction in the turret crew from three to two. The two versions were now classified as Marks I and II, but official doubts and the growing popularity of the Daimler combined to eclipse them. In August 1944 it was announced that the order for Mark Is would be reduced to 300 and that they would all go to India, while only two samples of the Mark II would appear. India probably never saw any of them, although after the war some were supplied to the French Army who took them to Indo-China, the only place in which they saw action.

34   An interesting course group photograph taken at Bovington after the war shows an AEC Mark II armoured car flanked by a 2-pounder Coventry I (left) and 75-mm Coventry II on the right.

35 A 37-mm gun Humber Mark IV armoured car of C Squadron, 15th (Scottish) Recce Regiment leading Nº 11 Troop, a mixed column of carriers and half-tracks, near the Belgian frontier in 1944.

36 The Rear Link version of the Humber Mark III, showing the generator housing and dummy guns.

37 A Humber scout car of 4th Armoured Brigade alongside a liberated Packard pick-up truck.

The decision to continue production of the Daimler armoured car instead of replacing it with the Coventry was taken midway through 1943. This provoked a series of detail improvements, mainly concerning the driver's hatch and engine armour, which was rearranged. The new model was styled Daimler Armoured Car Mark II, but no attempt was made to upgun it, beyond the fitting of a Littlejohn adaptor to some cars. This involved screwing a cone-shaped attachment to the muzzle of the gun which squeezed a super-velocity projectile that emerged at about twice the muzzle velocity of ordinary shot and more than double the penetrative power at short ranges.

Karrier Motors, producer of the Humber armoured car, had already moved to a Mark III model, of which 1,650 had been built when production ended late in 1942. It was characterised by a three-man turret but was otherwise similar to the Mark II. Indeed the change was effected without an increase in weight according to the records, which was probably just as well since the slightly lighter Mark I had been described as reliable yet underpowered when it was first tested in the Middle East in 1940. Pending the arrival of the Coventry, Karrier now embarked upon a Mark IV variant which would carry an American 37-mm gun to stiffen up the firepower of armoured car regiments. The extra turret crew member was sacrificed again and the car was described in an official document as 'not ideal', but with the demise of the Coventry it saw the war out and beyond, 2,000 being built. Many of the Mark IIIs were subsequently converted to the Rear Link role. This involved removing the armament and fitting a High Power No 19 wireless with its extra charging set. A prototype was completed in 1943 whereupon the first two production models were sent to Reo Motors for conversion. They were issued on the scale of two for each armoured car regiment and, as their name implies, provided improved long-range communications between front-line units and regimental headquarters. From late 1942 Humbers also became involved in scout car production. Theirs was nothing like as sophisticated as the Daimler, having a conventional chassis and rear mounted Super Snipe engine, but the fighting compartment at the front could house three men. Yet it seems to have been designed without any concession to current user requirements of the kind already expressed in North Africa concerning the Daimler. In the first place the body was entirely enclosed, with two small sliding hatches in the roof, while the floor was nothing more than mild steel where the crew sat, and non-existent beneath the engine, making it very vulnerable to mines. The armament of one Bren or two Vickers K guns was fitted to a device on the roof which could be operated by remote control from inside. The Humber was bigger, faster and slightly heavier than its Daimler counterpart, but with less than half of its armour protection, and it was decided that the three-man capacity suited it more to the intecommunication role while the Daimlers were retained for reconnaissance

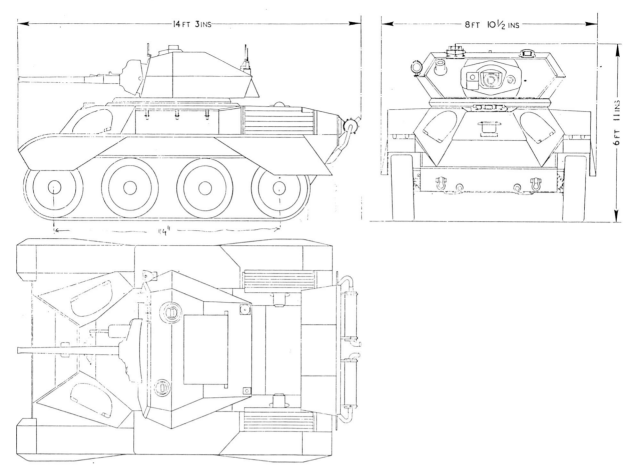

Drawing E: *Three-view drawing of the A25 Harry Hopkins.*

duties. Thus in North West Europe one found the Humbers more common in service with armoured divisions.

By the end of 1942 the light tank, at least the British light tank as exemplified by the A17 Tetrarch, was regarded as almost useless. Fifty of the hundred Tetrarchs produced had been supplied to Russia, while four of the remainder had been converted to mount the 3-inch howitzer, although at that stage nobody seemed to have much idea of what to do with them. Even so, the juggernaut of industry could not easily be stopped and by May of that year a new model was entering production. This was the A25, or Light Tank Mark VIII, named in honour of President Roosevelt's special advisor Harry Hopkins; what an honour! Like Tetrarch, it was a Vickers-Armstrong design built by Metro-Cammell and it shared with its predecessor a Meadows flat-twelve engine and the unusual track-warping system of steering. In this version, however, the steering was power assisted and the hull and turret were more effectively shaped from a ballistic point of view, although nobody could call it a good-looking tank.

Over 1,000 were on order, so the next stage was to decide what to use it for. A policy report issued in December 1942 suggested that it could be issued to reconnaissance regiments, or special light tank regiments raised for operations in what were described as 'suitable countries', possibly meaning mountainous regions and places like Madagascar which some Tetrarchs had invaded in the previous May. Ultimately the most popular suggestion was that they should be issued for airfield defence. In May 1943 the contract was reduced to 100 tanks, with a further 1,100 to be completed as Alecto 95-mm self-propelled guns. At the same time it was proposed to hand the 100 tanks over to the Royal Air Force, not only for defending airfields but also in connection with another, rather bizarre scheme. This was a device called the Carrier Wing, an idea that most tank-producing nations had toyed with before the war which involved fitting small tanks with a full set of flying surfaces so that they became little self-contained gliders. The object was to support airborne operations with flying tanks that could be towed by powered aircraft to the scene of operations and then released to find their own way down to the battle zone. The device proposed for the Harry Hopkins was an advanced type of glider known as the Allen Muntz Bat, but the project seems to have been dropped after a scale test model crashed. Attention then switched to a tank carried within a glider, the General Aircraft Hamilcar

38   *A 75-mm gun Valentine Mark XI, belonging to the Gunnery School at Lulworth Camp.*

which first flew in March 1942. For this, however, the 7.5 ton Tetrarch was preferred to the 8.5 ton Harry Hopkins and in the event the latter never saw service at all. Another possible explanation of its early demise is a Fighting Vehicle Proving Establishment report dated 9 July 1943 on user trials of the Harry Hopkins. Apparently serious defects occurred continually during the trial and the whole thing was abandoned at 598 miles, the normal span of such events being at least 2,000 miles. It was mentioned again by Vickers-Armstrong in October 1944 in connection with their proposed 16-ton AFV family, of which a close support reconnaissance member was described as a sort of turretless Harry Hopkins, although how this differed from an Alecto is impossible to tell.

The Crusader was declared obsolescent in 1943, apart from those earmarked as Observation Post or Anti-Aircraft tanks. The remainder would be phased out of service as new tanks arrived to replace them. A worse fate awaited the Covenanter. An official statement required that all except those converted into bridgelayers should be 'reduced to produce', in other words scrapped. Their infantry tank contemporaries generally fared better although the Valentine might be considered a curious survivor. In February 1942 the Tank Board had decided that any improvements to the tank should be left entirely to Vickers-Armstrong, and three months later the firm announced a new tank, to be known as Vampire, which would replace the Valentine. No specifications were given and the project was soon cancelled when it was believed

that Vickers would be drawn into the A27 Cruiser Tank programme. This fell through in its turn, and in order to avoid disruption on the production line it was agreed to continue building Valentines until the end of 1943, most of which were expected to be of the new Mark X specification.

The failing of the 6-pounder equipped Mark IX in not mounting a machine-gun has already been mentioned, and the Mark X was intended to remedy this, the 6-pounder turret being modified to incorporate a 7.62-mm Besa in separate trunnions on the right of the main gun. This installation displaced nine rounds of ammunition. Lulworth tested a production model in July 1943 and found the machine-gun very breech-heavy and lively, despite being balanced by two very long springs against the turret roof. They also criticised the limited stowage available for machine-gun ammunition and hand grenades. Certainly the two-man turret was dreadfully cramped, yet the tank remained popular for its low silhouette and, above all, its reliability. Obviously where the 6-pounder could go, the 75-mm would fit, so the final batch were completed as the Mark XI, production of which was said to be ceasing in a report dated December 1943. In the meantime another replacement was being developed under the name of Vanguard. That it was not a dramatic development is clear from the fact that some contemporary reports speak of the Valentine-Vanguard as if it were the same thing. Surviving details are few, although it is specified as weighing 16.5 tons against 17 tons for a late model Valentine. It was intended to carry a crew of three, a 6-pounder and Besa machine-gun, at a speed at least 8 mph faster than a Valentine. A pilot model is said to have been tested at some unspecified date in 1943 and these trials apparently revealed that the suspension was unsuitable, despite the fact that this appears to have been unchanged from the Valentine, beyond having equal-sized wheels. Vanguard was not proceeded with, due to the termination of the Valentine programme, although some parts developed for it were incorporated into the Archer SP anti-tank gun, and this may provide a clue to the Vanguard's appearance. The General Motors diesel engine in an Archer was rated at 192 hp, against 165 hp for the similar power pack in a Valentine XI. Comparing engine decks on the two types reveals that the SP gun has a raised central section not seen on the tanks, which may well have been connected with this increase in power and possibly, then, another identifying feature for Vanguard. In fact, apart from some DD amphibious tanks in Italy, and others supplied to self-propelled anti-tank batteries of the Royal Artillery, Valentines did not see active service as gun tanks with the British Army after the Axis surrender in Tunisia, yet production was actually considered beyond December 1943 on the grounds that it was potentially ideally suited to the Far East, an opinion possibly based on New Zealand Army experience, and it was still tremendously popular in the Soviet Union.

The Churchill programme for 1943 was mainly concerned with the continuing rework scheme and those developments already recorded in North Africa. In May 1943, when a further 1,000 tanks were ordered, it was agreed that production should continue through 1944, although this amounted to something approaching a new tank. This was the A22F (also designated A42 just to confuse things) or Heavy Churchill, which ultimately appeared as the Churchill Mark VII (75-mm) and Mark VIII (95-mm). The most important feature of the new tank was thicker armour, which at 6 in. (152 mm) on the front was actually thicker than that of the Tiger. Welded construction was employed throughout the hull and the side doors were made both rounded and slightly conical in section, as was the driver's visor. This had two advantages. In the first place a round opening does not create weak spots in the structure as the corners of a square one might, while the conical shape prevents them from being driven into the hull when hit from outside, which was a complaint levelled against the Mark IV. The main armament, naturally, was the new 75-mm gun, while the turret itself was an original design. Cast turrets, such as those fitted to the Churchill Mark IV, had many structural advantages but one problem was the manufacturer's inability to control material thickness effectively on all surfaces. Thus if one desired thick walls the roof could not be thin, so a weight and space penalty was inevitable. The new Heavy Churchill turret, apparently developed by Babcock and Wilcox of Renfrew, displayed a most

39 *Fitting the rear top-plate to the cast shell of an A22F Churchill turret at the Babcock & Wilcox foundry.*

effective compromise. The four sides were a single casting, flared out at the base to give added protection to the turret ring, while the roof was a flat plate welded into place at the top. The A22F was stated as meeting all requirements except in respect of armament.

With the appearance of the new tank – 700 having been ordered towards the end of 1943 – the rework programme for earlier models took on a new lease of life. This scheme had been applied to all but the first 247 tanks, which were retained for training, and was now expanded to include fitting of the 75-mm gun, a decision to convert as many as possible having been taken in February 1943. Yet it was a massive task. When they had been asked, back in November 1942, Vauxhall Motors had been unable to say how many different modifications had been applied to any individual tank. All they could say was that since the scheme had begun, a further 169 had been added of which forty were classed as essential, forty as desirable, and the rest of a minor character. These might include such things as drilling holes in the bottom of hand grenade containers to let water drain through. Granted this was a small matter that could be done virtually by anyone at any time, but that in itself raised another point. The Army claimed that due to shortages of technical personnel they could not undertake these modifications in the course of a regular overhaul, while Vauxhalls pointed out that they were often obliged to undertake a partial or even complete overhaul on a tank in order to effect a rework. To that extent the two functions were complementary. The upgunning process seems to have been aimed mainly at the cast-turreted Mark IV, which in its new guise became the Churchill Mark VI, although it was applied in a small way to the less-favoured Mark III with its welded turret. This, however, did not warrant the coining of a new mark beyond the designation Mark III*, or Mark III (75-mm). Although it takes us ahead somewhat, it is worth recording here that in July 1944 it was stated that all reworked

Churchills should have appliqué armour of ¾-in. thickness on the sides, and that by December this would include extra frontal armour along with gearbox, suspension and traverse equipment brought up to A22F specification and the fitting of a complete A22F turret. By August 1944 this last requirement had to be abandoned as impractical, at least for all reworks, due to a shortage of castings, and there is some question as to whether it was ever done at all. A whole new range of marks from IX to XIII was created to suit these new versions, and the tanks should have been readily identifiable by the combination of square doors on the hull with the cast/welded turret. None have ever been recognised from photographs or surviving tanks, and although this can hardly be regarded as conclusive evidence, it is worth noting that these later marks were also issued with the suffix LT, for Light Turret, and these can be recognised by the fitting of the new All Round Vision (ARV) cupola on the original cast turret. By late 1944 production of the Churchill Mark VII had been limited to one contractor, Vauxhall Motors, due to lowered requirements, and consideration was being given to cancellation of the entire programme. Thus the unwelcome upstart of 1940 had blossomed into one of the best British tanks of the war by 1944; how well it fared will be recorded later.

The British flair for improvisation is often cited when the subject of specialised armour is discussed, but if it is true it would seem to be a short-term trait. At least this is one conclusion which can be reached by anyone studying the subject in depth, when it becomes obvious that the same thing seems to be invented as the need arises, over and over again. In a major conflict, however, some sort of overall control is ultimately organised which can prevent duplication and ensure that unpromising projects are curtailed. In Britain, until March 1943, this was one purpose of the Anti-Tank Experimental Establishment at Aldershot, but at that time it was disbanded and reformed as the Obstacle Assault Centre. Its purpose was to develop techniques for the location and removal of minefields and means of overcoming physical obstacles. At the same time Major General Hobart, commanding the newly formed 79th Armoured Division, was told that this formation would now take over responsibility for organising all this equipment on an operational basis, a task which automatically involved drawing together the threads of all the other specialised armour projects being developed around the country. The obvious object of the entire project was to perfect as much equipment as possible in time for the proposed invasion of Europe.

The vehicle which formed the hub of the whole specialised armour concept was the AVRE, or Armoured Vehicle Royal Engineers. It evolved from a suggestion by Lieutenant J J Denovan, Royal Canadian Engineers attached to the Special Devices Branch of the Department of Tank

40 A damaged Churchill III, penetrated through the turret front, dangerously close to the dark shadow of the gun mounting, being recovered by a Diamond T tractor. Although this example retains the 6-pounder gun, panels of appliqué armour can be seen on the turret and hull sides.

Design. Based on Canadian engineers' reports of Dieppe he visualised a tank capable of transporting a party of sappers and their kit close enough to an objective to enable them to dismount and tackle it in relative safety. The obvious tank for this purpose was the Churchill, since it had side access doors and a tough hide. A prototype was therefore developed by 1st Canadian M E Company working on behalf of the DTD.

Towards the end of 1942 specifications for an Engineer Tank were laid out in the Half-Yearly Report of Progress by the Royal Armoured Corps. This explained that such a tank should be used solely for the engineering role and, as such, would not need a big gun. It should have a permanent crew of two, in addition to the sapper passengers and be of the same type of tank as the formation with which it was operating. It stated that two would be required for every tank regiment in an armoured division or brigade, the tanks being attached to the headquarters squadron. This was clearly not quite what the DTD had in mind. Early experiments involved making modifications to the Churchill's side doors so that they unfolded to provide extra cover for the crew, and a demonstration was staged on Hankley Common on 25 February 1943. The tank – a modified Churchill II with all its internal ammunition stowage ripped out – was driven up to a concrete wall and positioned where it shielded the sappers from imaginary enemy fire. They dismounted, emplaced General Wade explosive charges, lit them and retired to their tank which quickly made off. The resulting hole in the wall was big enough to drive a tank through. However at the same demonstration another weapon was shown

which reduced the risk to the engineers even further, this was the Petard.

Colonel Blacker, progenitor of that infamous Home Guard weapon the Blacker Bombard, was asked to design a similar spigot mortar to fire from a tank. His firm, Blacker Developments Ltd, of London came up with just the thing, which fired a 26-pounder high-explosive projectile known as the Flying Dustbin, which appeared to be capable of fearsome destructive powers. Unfortunately it exerted a recoil effect of about 20 tons, which would wreck the turret ring of a Churchill in no time. Efforts were therefore made to redesign it, and the result was a version with a recoiling spigot on an enormous spring which used up the reactionary effect by recocking the weapon. It was first tried in a redundant Covenanter and then fitted into a Churchill. Originally the purpose of the Petard was mine clearance, firing Flying Dustbins fused for air burst, and during the Hankley Common demonstration it cleared a path 28 ft wide through a minefield. It then moved up to the 6-ft thick reinforced concrete wall and, with twelve rounds fused for impact, created a gap large enough for a Churchill tank to drive through easily, without anyone having to dismount. Of course it worked at very short range. The maximum for the Petard was little over 200 yards, while 50 was preferred since it was not a highly accurate weapon. At Denovan's suggestion a powerful smoke shell was developed to screen sappers while they worked, which proved very effective. Some 700 Churchills Mark III and IV were converted to AVREs, initially by REME Workshops and subsequently by MG Cars of Abingdon using parts supplied by Cocksedge & Co of Ipswich. In keeping with the requirement to match AVRE to the tanks it was to mix with, a Sherman variant was proposed. In fact the first suggestion was to adapt the Canadian Ram, which could operate comfortably with Shermans, but by the time this project got under way it was learned that Rams were now being built without side doors, which was the reason for selecting it in the first place. Thus a Sherman AVRE was proposed, but then abandoned, when the organisational changes were introduced.

Of course the beauty of the AVRE was that, besides going around demolishing everything that got in its way, it could also be used as the carrier/launcher vehicle for a whole host of other devices – so many indeed that they cannot be dealt with in detail here. A set of universal brackets on the hull sides accepted most of these things. A typical example was the demolition charge. In addition to the Petard, described above, and Denovan's scheme to allow sappers to work from a tank, another idea to evolve from the Dieppe Raid was for a tank to lay a demolition charge on an obstacle automatically. The first, codenamed Carrot, was intended for use against minefields, employing the principle of sympathetic detonation. A small charge, up to 25 pounds, was suspended from a light framework on the front of a tank but heavier charges, up

41 *A member of a Churchill AVRE crew attaching the propulsion unit to a flying dustbin warhead alongside his tank. Just to the left is the bearing for a variety of attachments.*

to 600 pounds, were carried on an anti-mine roller pushed ahead of the tank. In order to detonate, the tank had to leave the entire assembly, roller attachment and charge, in the minefield and then retreat, but it was a costly way of doing the job and did not work very well.

Onion, which was developed as a direct result of the Dieppe raid, was designed for use in conjunction with the Churchill AVRE. Arms attached to brackets on the sides of the tank supported a vertical framework with a pair of hinged legs at the back. Explosive charges were arranged on the outer face of the frame in a pattern to suit the intended target, which the tank then approached. At the desired spot it released the frame, whose legs now swung down, forcing it forwards against the obstacle, while the tank backed away, trailing the ignition cable. Once it had retired to a safe distance the tank then exploded the charge. The Onion frame was also tested as a means of carrying two lengths of Bangalore Torpedo which it dropped into wire entanglements and detonated, as well as the stangely named Quinson Device. Not even the *Oxford English Dictionary* recognises the word Quinson, but the demolition device so named was arranged to be hung over the top of a wall, which at least did away with the problem of making it stay there. Onion worked well enough against Dragon's Teeth tank traps and steel beach obstacles, but not against walls or pillboxes because the frame did not always position itself effectively, so it too was dropped.

Next came the device codenamed Goat, which was designed to ensure the maximum accuracy in placing. For a start it was carried horizontally so that the tank driver had a better view of where he was going. It also rested on four attachment points to the tank, to ensure greater lateral stability. Two prongs, extending from the front of the frame, would be activated when they touched the obstacle so there was no need for the tank driver to judge

distance too carefully. These prongs caused the frame to pivot automatically to the upright position, whereupon the tank pressed it up against the obstacle and backed away, leaving it anchored by a pair of sprags. This worked well enough to warrant production and 400 were made. Elevatable Goat was another development which could be emplaced to straddle a much higher wall than the Quinson Device could reach. A diminutive of Goat, designed to fit the Universal Carrier, was inevitably known as Kid.

Another standard AVRE attachment was the Carpet Device. Once again an exact counterpart can be discovered in the First World War although it was never adopted. A crude version had been used in the Dieppe landing, but the Combined Operations Executive wished to develop it, mainly with a view to laying a path across wire entanglements. The tank supported a large frame upon which was a drum, the full width of the tank, around which was wrapped a carpet of hessian, strengthened at intervals with

43   *A Churchill Mark IV demonstrating the Bobbin carpet-laying device.*

42   *A Churchill AVRE, with full deep-wading gear fitted, approaching a wall with its Goat demolition device, during trials in North Devon.*

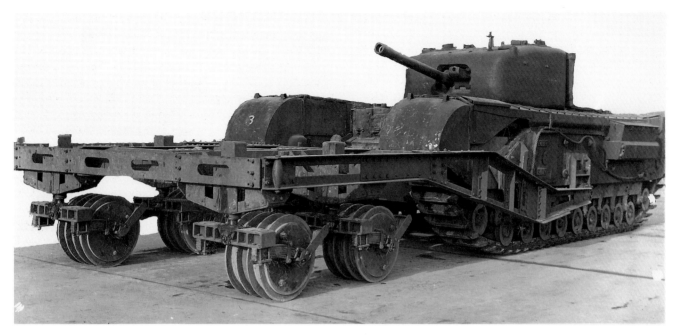

44 *The Anti-Mine Roller, Castoring Roller equipment fitted to a Churchill Mark IV.*

scaffolding poles. On arriving at the wire the other end of this mat was dropped, the tank ran on to it and unwound it as it proceeded through the wire. Once the carpet had all run off, the tank detached itself from the framework and went about its business. Early trials were not very promising. Where the wire was firmly held down by pickets the carpet worked well, but if it was loose the whole thing simply sprung up again behind the tank and became useless for infantry or wheeled vehicles to follow. The ultimate version, codenamed rather obviously Bobbin, used spring-loaded extension pieces which shot out from either side of the carpet as it was laid and by extending the area so covered made a better job of it. In addition to wire, the carpet was effective for a while against patches of very soft sand or clay which would otherwise immobilise a tank, although it soon got chewed up by the tracks, if it was not washed away by the incoming tide. Carpet and other tracklaying devices were also developed to fit the Universal Carrier but one feels the problem here would be the useful length of mat that could be carried on such a small vehicle.

Anti-mine rollers have already been mentioned, but it is worth stressing again that they were not intended so much as a means of clearing minefields as of detecting them. Flails or ploughs did a much better job of clearing mines, but you could not flail or plough up an entire battlefield – that would be vastly extravagant in materials and impossibly time-consuming. Thus where mines were suspected, other than in an identifiable minefield, the idea was for a tank, propelling rollers in front of it to precede the other vehicles until its rollers detonated a mine. The Anti-Mine Reconnaissance Castor Roller device described this function in its title. Early examples, as used in the desert, were

not 100 per cent successful because the roller was rigidly mounted, but the AMRCR, developed by the Obstacle Assault Centre, used sprung rollers which were far more sensitive to ground. To quote the Handbook, 'The Device is considerably less unwieldy than first impressions may suggest. It reacts immediately to all movements of the tank, and with practice can be driven over practically any type of country that the tank itself is capable of negotiating.' It was designed to fit all Marks of Churchill, and with little adaption also the Sherman V (M4A4), but it was most commonly associated with the Churchill AVRE. The OAC also developed a system whereby the tank could tow the device when not required, but this failed to come up to expectations and was abandoned.

As a means of disposing of mines with a tank, the use of a plough had been popular since before the war. By the spring of 1943 the firm Samuel Butler Ltd, of Leeds had produced an amazingly complicated device known as Farmer Front which covered the entire width of the tank. This not only required an inordinate amount of power to push it through the ground, but it also evinced a nasty habit of trying to nose-dive into it. It was replaced by Farmer Track which only turned up the ground in front of each track, but it still had a tendency to bury itself in the process, and was likewise dropped in December 1943. In the mean time the OAC, in conjunction with Ransomes, Simms & Jefferies of Ipswich, came up with Farmer Deck. Whereas the two earlier types used a mass of slim tines, this third model was provided with ploughshares to turn up the mines. Each blade was also preceded by a roller which, in theory, prevented it from digging in too far but instead, it was discovered, the ploughshares tended to crush the mines, which was no good either.

To the professional soldier or civil servant trying to get things done in an organised way small cliques of inventors are as much trouble as private armies. To students of the weird and wonderful they are a blessing, not only for the strange ideas they throw up but also for the odd characters they attract. One such was Major Millis Rowland Jefferis RE, whose small department in Portland Place was mostly concerned with sabotage. He could have been closed down quite early in the war, were it not for the fact that he was admired by the Prime Minister, but how he got into the business of tank-mounted mine ploughs has never been explained. The fact is that a mine plough is relatively prosaic, just a variation on an agricultural theme, and it is simply a matter of getting the right arrangement of coulters or tines to make it work – hardly the kind of thing an explosives expert should need to get involved in. Even so, Jefferis' organisation did get involved and the result was a lightweight plough known as the MD1 (MD for Minister of Defence, an office held by the Prime Minister). For trials purposes it was attached to Churchill and Sherman tanks, and a report of the time explained that much less power was needed to propel it than an ordinary plough and that speeds of up to 5 mph could be reached, while it could turn up Teller mines buried 12 in. deep. Unfortunately it then tended to let the mines fall back into the tank's tracks, which was hardly the point of the exercise.

The Teller mine was the real bogey for all these projects. Ultimately the most effective of these devices was the Bullshorn Plough which went through three phases of development, by 79th Armoured Division themselves who named it after their famous badge, the Bull's Head. It ploughed in front of the tank's tracks only, cutting furrows 12 in. deep and nearly 2 ft wide at between 2 and 4 mph. It could be mounted on any Sherman or Churchill, using fittings on the front of the hull, although in practice it was intended for use with an AVRE. In its Mark III form it was the only type of plough to be employed on operations. The one remaining problem was the mines left in the gap between the furrows. The ploughing tank would pass over these quite harmlessly but the next vehicle, unless it followed acurately in the first tank's

path, was in obvious danger. In an effort to eliminate this danger Ransomes, Simms & Jefferies designed a harrow which was towed by the ploughing tank. For reasons that defy explanation it was known as the Senior Equitine Cultivator. The word Equitine is another which has never been picked up by the *Oxford English Dictionary*, unless it is a corruption of equine, meaning of, or like a horse. There is a certain vague logic in this, for the device looks as if it would have been quite at home on a 19th-century farm. It could turn up Teller mines from a depth of 18 in. and the only drawback the investigators could find in it was that a crew member had to dismount from the tank in order to lower the tines for ploughing.

The technique of disposing of mines by sympathetic detonation has already been mentioned. Teller mines were very susceptible to this and were normally sown at least 7 ft apart to prevent it from happening. Firing Petards at them worked, as we have seen, while Snake was an

46 *A Sherman used to demonstrate Colonel Jefferis' MD1 mine plough on a beach.*

47 *A Sherman V of 79th Armoured Division demonstrating a Bullshorn anti-mine plough device at the Obstacle Assault Centre.*

45 *Farmer Track mine plough on a Churchill Mark IV.*

alternative, if unwieldy way of doing this. It consisted of lengths of scaffolding pipe packed with explosive which were connected up to the depth of field to be covered. The control tank then dragged the pipe up to the edge of the minefield, reversed to attach itself to the rear end and then pushed it into the danger zone. Once the charge was in place the tank backed away, trailing the detonating lead through its hull floor escape hatch, and set the thing off from a safe distance. Apart from the fact that Snake was unwieldily to handle, it also had an awkward habit, when being pushed, of wandering off at a tangent on uneven ground.

Without a doubt, of all the options available, the most effective mechanical means of destroying mines was a rotary flail propelled by a tank. By 1943 the Matilda Baron, developed independently of the Scorpion in the Middle East, had reached a Mark III version but it was plagued with minor faults and, in any case, was too wide to use a landing craft. Britain now realised that the Scorpion was a much simpler answer to the problem and, having tried and failed to get the army in Egypt to rename their product Baron, elected to copy it and adopt the name Scorpion after all. AEC Ltd of Southall undertook the development work and produced a package that could be manufactured separately and then fitted to a tank simply by removing the turret and adding a few brackets. The tank selected was the Valentine, and in converted form it was known as the UK Scorpion Mark III. The turret was replaced by a complex superstructure which housed the tank commander and flail operator along with two Ford V8 engines which drove a skeletal flail drum at the end of a pair of lattice girder arms. Since any mark of Valentine could be converted, there was again the fuel problem imposed by a diesel tank with petrol-driven flail to consider in some instances.

The first prototype was completed in April 1943, but during an early trial it detonated one Teller mine which set off another beneath the hull by sympathetic detonation and killed the crew of three. As a consequence extra plating was provided for the second prototype, and when a goat survived a similar incident in this, the type was adopted for service. Twenty-five sets of Scorpion equipment were made by T C Jones & Co., of Shepherds Bush and the tanks started to enter service in the summer of 1943.

In 1942 the South African flail pioneer, Major du Toit, working in conjunction with AEC Ltd, put forward the idea of a perambulator flail, in which the device was supported independently of the tank and pushed around by it. It failed at that stage but was revived by Samuel Butler Ltd in 1943, with an important innovation. This was that the flail drum should be driven off the tank's front drive sprockets (a Sherman was therefore essential) thus removing the need for a secondary engine housing. A prototype known as the Pram Scorpion was completed in May 1943 and submitted for trials. The rotor arms were

48 A Valentine Scorpion flail. The superstructure houses two of the crew and a pair of Ford V8 engines.

49 A Sherman Pram Scorpion showing the exposed chain drive to the flail and the rollers that support the boom.

50 A Sherman Marquis flail with the boom elevated.

hinged to the tank's leading suspension units, but most of the weight was taken by a set of castor rollers on a sub-frame, and quite a lot of weight it was, the entire unit tipping the scales at 4 ton 6 cwt. It also stuck out well ahead of the tank and, if it has any bearing on the matter, looked very untidy. The exposed chain drive from sprocket to rotor was very complicated, and no doubt

51 *A Sherman Crab I. The wire-cutting blades can be seen on each end of the rotor.*

vulnerable. Since the rotor was required to spin much faster than the tank tracks were turning, two step-down links were incorporated in the drive train, which meant a total of three loops of chain and four sprockets, but that was not all. Since the rotor was driven by both sprockets it is clear that when the tank turned the drive to each end of the rotor would be at a different speed, and in order to overcome that the rotor itself was split at the middle so that each half could rotate at a speed to match. Trials revealed endless mechanical problems, notably with the castors which also set up considerable rolling resistance, so as soon as it became clear that comething better was in the offing the scheme was abandoned with very few trials ever taking place.

By the summer of 1943 flail invention was reaching something of a frenzy and, with the exception of the Pram Scorpion, all of the competing design work was being done by AEC Ltd, which must have been a very unusual state of affairs. Thus, even while they were working on the design of the ultimately successful Crab, they were also trying to adapt the UK Scorpion system to Sherman. It was not just a matter of keeping the project up to date in terms of tanks, there was also a requirement for the jib to be raised and lowered hydraulically so that flail tanks stowed on board a landing craft could snuggle up closer to one another and save deck space. To avoid confusion with the Middle East it was now decided to drop the name Scorpion

and go for something else. Octopus was rejected, and the Baronial flavour retained by calling it Marquis. Eleven extra prototypes were ordered for comparative purposes with Crab, but the latter was so obviously better that only the original Marquis prototype was completed, and proved to be very effective.

The Sherman Crab design was initiated by AEC Ltd in answer to the Pram Scorpion because they, too, could see the sense of a flail driven somehow by the tank's own engine instead of fitting an extra one. The first prototype was completed in September 1943. It was seen at once that the flail support arms were too flimsy, but work went ahead in order to prove the principle. A loop of roller chain from the tank's drive shaft passed through the right side of the hull into a housing where it turned a cardan shaft, from the forward end of which another shaft engaged bevel gears at the end of the rotor. It was simple, compact and, since flailing was only done in first gear, sufficiently powerful. The production prototype, which was completed in October, featured stronger flail arms and hydraulic lifting gear derived from Marquis, with the same purpose in mind. The drum rotor on this model also had Baron type wire cutters at each end, reintroduced for the first time. By November 1944, orders for 300 Crabs had been placed with a variety of firms for delivery by March 1944. The subsequent story of the Crab is long and involved, but we shall leave it there for the present.

52 *A UK-Pattern Churchill ARK I wedged up against a training wall at Woodbridge, Suffolk. A spare fascine is lying close by and extra ramps have been placed at the back.*

Although the ARK was invented more or less by accident in Italy, the concept had been tested in Britain well before the war, but never developed. Revival of the idea is credited to Colonel S G Galpin, Commandant of the Experimental Bridging Establishment at Christchurch. Hearing of the new Churchill AVRE, but without having seen one, Galpin came up with a proposal for towing a set of tracked ramps behind the AVRE which other tanks would use to climb up and over the engineer tank when faced with an obstacle like a very high wall. Of course, once he realised that the engineer tank was going to have a turret, Galpin dropped the idea.

The next revival was due to 79th Armoured Division, faced with the task of getting tanks ashore on the Normandy beaches and then across the substantial sea wall that faced them. Using a turretless Churchill hull they naturally came up with something very similar to the Italian Pattern ARK, except that they decided to run trackways the full length of the vehicle, instead of permitting track-to-track contact. This was clearly because the anticipated role was so different. A British ARK, on approaching a sea

53 *A Churchill Mark IV makes a dramatic departure from a trial wall having climbed up over a sister tank fitted with Major Lakeman's ARK attachment.*

wall, would first drop a small fascine if that wall was vertical, or tackle it direct if it sloped, and then attempt to scrabble up as far as it could. Here it would rest and drop its longer rear ramps to the ground. Following tanks would then clamber up, over its back and across stubby forward ramps on to the promenade. Even using an ARK the climb was quite a steep one and the climbing tank would probably have slipped off if there were only metal-to-metal contact. Thus the runways, like the ramps, were provided with regularly spaced cross-members, which the tracks of the climbing tank could grip more easily. Fifty Mark II and IV Churchill hulls, not required for the Canal Defence Light programme (see later in the book), were modified into ARKs by REME workshops and the MG Car Company using superstructure kits made by T C Jones & Co.

Just because Brigadier Galpin believed that a turreted ARK was impossible, that did not mean that someone would not try it. That someone was Major Tom Lakeman, a rather eccentric RTR officer who spent half his time on somewhat dubious inventions and the rest at loggerheads with many of his contemporaries, superiors and anyone else who appeared to get in his way. In this instance his invention, if not entirely practical, was certainly impressive. It could be fitted to any turreted Churchill or AVRE and consisted of a ramped superstructure which ran up from hinged ramps at the back of the tank, levelled out above the turret to end roughly in line with the front of the carrier tank. Naturally the supports for the ramp were of a substantial nature, especially at the front where they had to bear the weight of the overhanging ramps themselves and a fully laden Churchill tank that might want to pass over them. Lakeman argued that with his arrangement the

tank was still free to fire within a 270 degree arc, although great care would be needed to avoid blasting away the uprights, and in any case a Churchill with the ramps in place weighed over 44 tons. Not surprisingly it was abandoned at the prototype stage.

Once Colonel Galpin had seen a Churchill AVRE he approached the sea wall problem from a different angle. Rather than make the tank into a ramp, he elected to have the standard AVRE carry one and emplace it against the obstacle. The ramp was in fact a shortened version of the 34-ft Small Box Girder Bridge developed at Christchurch before the war. Its nearer end rested upon brackets on the nose of a Churchill AVRE and it was then raised, roughly to an angle of 45 degrees, by a manually operated winch at the rear of the tank's engine deck. Braced by cables acting as stays, it hung in this precarious position, seriously upsetting the balance of the unfortunate tank as it drove up to the obstacle. Since the whole object of the exercise was to lay the bridge under fire the crew were not supposed to resort to the winch to lower it in place, but rather to let it drop, after activating a quick-release mechanism adapted from an RAF bomb-release device, directly above the turret. There were plenty of disadvantages. The strain on the tank's front bogies was enormous and progress was painfully slow, even on level ground. If the bridge started to sway, the tank set up a waddling motion which got progressively worse until the bridge broke away. For this reason, crossing uneven ground was almost impossible. Secondly, great care had to be taken near overhead wires and it was quite impossible for the vehicle to pass beneath any overbridge on its route. If the bridge were simply to be rested against a wall or similar obstacle it could be released with some confidence, but if it

54   Churchill AVREs of 42nd Assault Regiment, Royal Engineers, preparing for the attack on Le Havre. Sepoy on the left carries a Small Box Girder bridge. The tank has a small fascine at the front and a winch assembly at the back.

were to be used across a ditch or shell hole, the chances of dropping it accurately were very slim indeed. Yet there was one significant advantage. If the bridge was successfully emplaced it could be left where it was, still serving its purpose, while the AVRE could carry on the fight.

Genuine tank bridgelayers have already been mentioned. The Covenanter and Valentine scissors bridgelayers both saw active service, the former only with the Australians, the latter by everyone else right through to the end of the war. Late in 1942 the Experimental Bridging Establishment at Christchurch developed a prototype on the Churchill tank. It carried the 34-ft No 2 tank bridge which, because the tank was long enough to handle it, was not of the folding type. The Churchill hull was lightened as much as possible, with reduced thickness of armour on less vulnerable parts, and the bridge was carried, correct way up, on top of the hull.

The launching mechanism was hydraulic, with a boom that supported the bridge at its point of balance and rested on the ground during the launching cycle which, at the recommended engine speed, took 1 minute 35 seconds. It was just as easy for a tank to pick up its bridge as lay it, and the bridge itself was rated at 40 tons capacity. The tank had a crew of three, since wireless was now deemed essential for bridgelayers, and the commander had a small armoured conning tower to work from. Known colloquially as Jumbos, Churchill bridgelayers were regarded as RAC, not RE equipment and issued on the scale of three per brigade. In 1943 the requirement was stated as 200, but this was reduced to 64 by the end of the year and they were all recorded as in service by mid-1944.

Tank flamethrower development got into its stride in March 1942, with the amalgamation of design teams from the Petroleum Warfare Department and Ministry of Supply. The former devised a system in which the flame was activated by gas pressure, while the MoS method employed cordite and twelve examples of each, to fit Valentine tanks, had been ordered for training. In future the General Staff wished the combined teams to concentrate on the pressure method and, by the end of the year, a prototype based on a Churchill tank was running. It had been hoped to include the flame fuel reservoir and gas bottles within the tank itself, but when the projected weight proved prohibitive it was agreed to resort to a trailer for the fuel and propellant which the tank would tow, as in both Valentine versions. The first model appeared on a Churchill II and on trial managed to project flame for 200 yards, which was vastly superior to any previous efforts.

By early 1943 further trials proved that the trailer was no great hindrance to the tank and six prototypes were ordered for fitting to Churchill Mark IV tanks, which were expected to become the main production model of what was now being called the Crocodile. There was also talk of a heavily armoured trailer, since its contents were both vulnerable and lethal, but this was abandoned in favour of one built to 14-mm standard. At the same time, work began on the design of a Sherman Crocodile which, like the Churchill, would mount its flame projector in the hull machine-gun position, and the US Army announced a tentative order for 125 such devices.

The Crocodile had now become high priority, so in order to expedite matters it was agreed that all heavy Churchills (A22F) would be modified to accept the flame equipment while on the production line, so that the actual conversion could, if necessary, be undertaken in the field. The order for Crocodiles was now placed, amounting to 250 units, and it was stated that they would be issued to all units equipped with the Churchill Mark VII, although no scale was given at this time. By the summer of 1944 the Sherman Crocodile was being referred to as an American project, suggesting that they had taken over development, although this seems unlikely. Prototype trials had indicated a need to shift the flame projector on this tank from the hull Browning mount to a position just above it, alongside the gunner's hatch.

55 *A Churchill Bridgelayer with the bridge about midway through its launching cycle.*

56 *The original Churchill II Crocodile demonstrating its cross-country ability.*

Reports from Europe after D-Day showed that the device had proved very successful, although it had now been decided to operate regiments specifically dedicated to the Churchill Crocodile, which were soon absorbed into 79th Armoured Division. The worst faults reported were loss of pressure in the propellant, leaking fuel from the trailer and a nasty tendency to brew up if the tank was hit near the flame projector location.

In an attempt to improve handling the PWD also developed a smaller, single-wheeled, castor-action trailer for the Crocodile but, following demonstrations for the General Staff in the summer of 1943 it was abandoned. At that point the Royal Engineers took it up as a potential AVRE trailer, since it had an internal capacity of 45 cubic feet, but that project was also abandoned fairly quickly. At the other end of the scale from Crocodile in the flamethrowing role was Wasp, based on the Universal Carrier. The original Ronson project having been taken over by the Canadians, R P Fraser of Lagonda designed a new installation for the Carrier which was known as Wasp. In response to General Staff requirements on vulnerability, the fuel tank was stowed inside the hull, but any chance of anonymity was upset by the huge flame projector mounted above the armour. Fraser's brief had been to produce a flamethrower with greater range than the Ronson and in his second version of the Wasp he excelled himself with a design that had two fuel tanks within the hull, a projector mounted in the Carrier's regular weapon slot and a maximum effective range of 100 yards. Known as the Wasp Mark II it was adopted for service with infantry battalions in most theatres of war, while the original Mark I version was relegated to training.

Early developments in the Canal Defence Light saga were recounted in the previous volume (*The Great Tank Scandal*, p 126). By January 1943 there were two regiments equipped with Matilda CDL, fitted with the 65-mm thick turret and one regiment (152nd RAC) which had Churchills mounting the new 85-mm armoured turret. Neither tank was ideal for the purpose. As a CDL the Matilda only carried a crew of two, and in any case it was rapidly going out of production while the Churchill, ideal in every other respect, did not provide its driver with a wide enough view when operating with the light. The total requirement for CDLs in British service at home and in the Middle East, calculated on a regimental strength of forty-two tanks plus 50 per cent reserves, was 567 machines. General Staff policy on the equipment called, among other things, for a turret capable of mounting CDL and a normal offensive armament, and that the CDL tank should look as much like any other tank as possible. The only way that the Directorate of Armoured Fighting Vehicles could see of achieving this was to use the M3 Grant, which could take the 65-mm CDL in place of its normal 37-mm gun turret while retaining its 75-mm hull weapon. Whether, by 1943, it had a silhouette that resembled a normal tank is another matter.

57 *A carrier-borne Wasp flamethrower showing the projector in the front compartment and two fuel tanks alongside the engine in the back.*

58 *Grant CDLs training on the Cumbrian fells.*

Once a Grant or Lee tank loses its turret the difference is almost academic, and since so many tanks were needed it did not pay to be fussy. British training establishments and Canadian forces in Britain were required to hand in 126 Grants and Lees for conversion. The United States were asked to supply 252 Lees or Grants, if they still held any of the latter, while in the Middle East 189 more Lees and Grants were to be prepared for conversion. In passing it is worth noting that in Britain the CDL was regarded with a degree of secrecy that verged upon paranoia, with the two brigades established being virtually incommunicado in their Cumbrian fastness. In the Middle East, by contrast, CDL regiments were integrated with normal formations. Knowing that they would not be the first to use this equipment operationally, Middle East Command intended to be ready for active service as soon as the veil of secrecy was lifted.

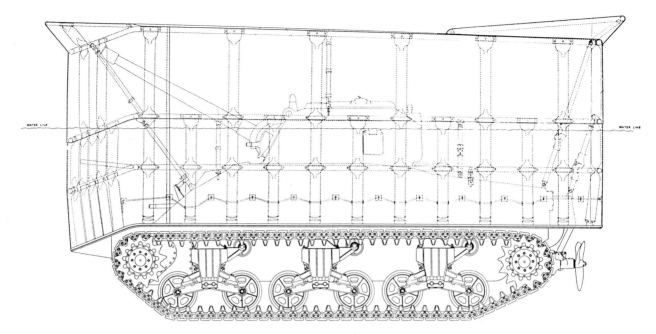

Drawing F: *Diagram showing Straussler's DD attachment on a Sherman. As well as the screen supports, the rear sprocket and propellor can also be seen.*

Following the successful development of the Valentine Duplex Drive swimming tank, a total of 450 were ordered, of which the first 214 would be equipped with the 2-pounder gun, although all would be of the General Motors diesel-engined type. The designers then turned their attention to a DD version of Cromwell, but this project was postponed until that tank should be considered battleworthy on land, and in the event work on a DD Cromwell lapsed. So did a scheme mentioned in 1943 to adapt the equipment to suit the Churchill. Instead, the War Office made it known that they wished the device to be developed to fit the Sherman and, as a first step, an M4A4 (Sherman V) was adapted. The main problem to be overcome was not flotation – given enough displacement (which in essence meant the height of the skirt), any tank could be made to swim – rather it was one of transmission. The engine and gearbox layout of the Sherman prevented it from adopting the Valentine's Duplex system of a power take-off from the transmission. Instead it was decided to drive the propellor from the tracks, via the rear idler, and it therefore proved possible to incorporate two propellors, giving an enhanced performance in the water.

American interest in the project led to the creation of a Sherman IV (M4A3) DD and, again for British users, a diesel Sherman III (M4A2) model. Meanwhile a Valentine Mark IX DD appeared for use in the Far East but 105 (seventy-five operational, thirty training) were also supplied to British forces in Italy. By late 1944 a Valentine XI DD existed; some were sent to India for training purposes. By December 1944 the total number of Sherman DDs delivered was 293 of the Sherman III and 400 of the Sherman V, by which time they had proved themselves,

more or less, in action.

As fast as any weapon is developed, someone else is thinking up ways of destroying it and two potentially devastating methods were suggested for the DD tank, explosion and fire. The former was tested by detonating a 309-pound charge of amatol within 100 yards of a floating DD – in effect, a depth charge – but it was not found to harm the tank or its occupants. Flame was another matter. Years earlier, when invasion had threatened, a marine flame barrage had been installed on the Dorset coast which was supposed to burn invaders in their boats. Just in case the Germans had invented something similar this was reactivated in 1944 to test the flammability of DD tanks. In order to reduce the risk, something called Counter DD (later Belch) was developed. It consisted of a small motor-driven pump, installed on the rear deck of the tank, that pumped seawater through a pipe running round the top of the screen which was perforated at ten points to create a spray that soaked the screen. It worked well enough on trial, although it was reasoned that unless the sea was millpond calm the screen would be quite wet enough anyway and the fitting was never employed, although 120 sets of the equipment were ordered. Flame, however, was not restricted to the sea and a fear now arose over the use of flamethrowers against DD tanks on land. All the while the screen remained wet it proved to be no problem, even with flamethrowers with the power of Wasp. But dry, raised or folded, it could be disastrous. Since there was no way of keeping a screen soaking wet on land it was recommended that it be cut off at the first opportunity after landing, although in practice the threat never seems to have materialised.

59 *A Sherman DD at Stokes Bay near Gosport demonstrating the Belch device. The water intake can be seen on the ground at the back.*

Very little is known about some devices referred to in reports as DD Tenders. They are described as 'decoy vehicles, built to resemble in appearance a Duplex Drive vehicle, but with no armament and a crew of one man'. Further it is said that they had the same speed as a DD tank, an operational range of one hour and an ability to work in the same conditions as a DD tank. By late 1943 orders had been placed for fifty of these, half Valentine, half Sherman. Use of the word vehicle, and mention of the two tanks, leads one to visualise a turretless DD tank with just its driver for crew, but such a craft would be impossible to operate because the driver would not be able to see where he was going, and without considerable modification could not steer the thing either, blind or not. In fact it seems that they were a form of collapsible boat, complete with outboard motor, that looked like a DD tank in the water, although why anyone should bother to create Valentine and Sherman types in those circumstances defies comprehension.

Operational experience with DD tanks at sea, especially by the Americans, indicated that improved seaworthiness and a more rigid screen would be essential. Modifications were introduced which included self-locking struts, an enlarged apron at the stern to give more freeboard and two extra struts amidships which held the top rail firm against the turret. Further developments by the originator, Nicholas Straussler, included greater freeboard forward, a stronger top rail, improved bilge pump, hydraulic instead of manual steering in the water and an air compressor to replace the air bottles originally used to inflate the screen. From late 1944 it was hoped to build all DDs to this Mark II standard while 120 conversion kits were supplied for the earlier model (now DD I) and despatched to South East Asia Command.

Further DD developments will be covered in subsequent chapters. Here it only remains to record one of the more dubious variants. This was Dragonfly, a miniature DD version of the Universal Carrier with Ronson flamethrower. Six were built and tested first on a pond near Beaulieu in the New Forest. The method of propulsion in the water is not recorded but following sea trials in the Solent, where they seem to have performed reasonably well, the scheme was abandoned – not, one feels, without the occasional sigh of relief.

4 The new enemy

There can be few greater contrasts in topography than that between the raw, hot expanse of the Libyan Desert and the close, humid, snake-infested Burmese jungle. Neither can one detect much similarity, as enemies – at least as they were perceived at the time – between the prudent, disciplined Germans and manic, almost suicidal Japanese. Yet the 2nd Royal Tank Regiment and 7th Hussars, forming the reduced 7th Armoured Brigade, exchanged the former for the latter in both cases in little over a month, early in 1942. Both regiments had been re-equipped entirely with M3 series Stuart tanks to meet the emergency created by the Japanese invasion of Malaya; the situation changed so rapidly that they were diverted to Rangoon *en route* and even found that city on the point of collapse when they landed.

60   *A Stuart of 2nd RTR during its short combat career in Burma.*

61   *Indian Pattern Carriers; a turreted Mark IIC in the foreground and a turretless version beyond.*

Riding the crest of a wave of military success, combined with a massive psychological advantage, the Japanese would soon sweep the British out of Burma, and there was very little two regiments of light tanks would be able to do about it. It was not a matter of superior equipment, nor in any respect of courage, but largely one of technique. It would simply have been asking too much to have expected these regiments to forget what the desert had taught them about wide flanking sweeps and long-range gunfights, in a five-week voyage, and to adjust at once to a road-bound campaign, in thick jungle against a wily enemy who never thought twice about charging a tank with a mine on the end of a long pole, or of clambering on board while it was moving, to throw a phial of sleeping gas into the turret. Thus the armoured brigade moved north through Burma with the British Army in what was, at one and the same time, both an advance and a retreat. They crossed over the Chindwin, leaving all but one of their surviving tanks on the south bank, and thence into India, from where they subsequently returned to the Western Desert.

Armoured vehicle development in India, following the period of experimentation chronicled in the first volume of this work (*The Great Tank Scandal*, p 99), settled down from 1942 to concentrate on developments of the Canadian Ford-based wheeled carriers. The main production version of the Indian Pattern Wheeled Carrier was the Mark II. Compared with the prototype Mark I it used Canadian Military Pattern components based on the Ford Quad artillery tractor, but with a rear-engine layout. This led to an unusual state of affairs whereby drive was always available on the front axle with the rear one only brought into play when four-wheel drive was engaged. The slope-fronted, armoured hull was formed from 14-mm plate. It was open at the top and provided room for a crew of four. Firepower was limited to portable weapons such as the Bren gun. Some British regiments in India record delivery of one or two of these vehicles with mock-up wooden bodies, presumably for user appreciation, in February 1942. According to the 26th Hussars war diary, their two were returned two months later for armouring. The main production version was the Mark IIA, which saw service not only in India and Burma, but throughout the Middle East and Italy as well. It was followed by a Mark IIB which had some overhead armour protection, while the Mark IIC was similar with an improved chassis. A version of this model also featured a small turret for the Bren gun, in the Armoured Observation Post role.

The Mark III came complete with a much larger turret

62   *An Indian Pattern Carrier Mark IV on British Army service in Calcutta after the war. The armoured driver's cab can be seen to the left.*

which could mount a Boys anti-tank rifle in addition to the Bren gun and where these were issued to British regiments they were often referred to as armoured cars, rather than carriers, although this was hardly justified. Very little can be discovered about their immunity to mines, but it cannot have been very good because all models described so far had wood-planked floors in the fighting compartment. The last version, the Mark IV, was designed towards the end of 1942. It was lower at the front, with a separate armoured cab for the driver, but this layout seriously reduced the space available for the rest of the crew and, following complaints that they were cramped, production appears to have been discontinued. Even so, some British regiments operating in the Far East after the war certainly had the Mark IV version and employed them on internal security duties.

The Indian Armoured Corps was formed on 1 May 1941. At first many of its regiments had nothing more to train on than battered, conscripted civilian lorries, but when the Japanese threat materialised, tanks, mostly of American origin, were forthcoming. Yet this took time to implement and in order to provide some armour for Malaya the Indian 3rd Cavalry Regiment was despatched to Singapore via Penang to be equipped with thirty Marmon-Herrington Mark III armoured cars in December 1941. Here it was joined by the 100th Independent Light Tank Squadron which took over nine Bren Carriers, reputedly already worn out in the Middle East. Neither unit had any experience of their vehicles, but before any training could be organised they were in action. The 3rd Cavalry took the fight to the enemy, along with some aged

Lanchester armoured cars of the Argyll and Sutherland Highlanders, but the survivors were soon forced back to Singapore, only to be included in General Percival's surrender on 14 February 1942.

Two days before Singapore fell, the *SS Hermion* docked at the port of Oosthaven in Sumatra. It was carrying a squadron of Light Mark VIB tanks of the 3rd Hussars, diverted there while on course for Singapore. In 1940, it may be recalled, it was the 3rd Hussars who had supplied some light tanks to another folorn hope, the defence of Norway. These tanks had been lost at sea and now history was almost to repeat itself. Sumatra was soon a lost cause but, their original ship having sailed, the squadron was transferred to Java after a perilous voyage. Here, along with some American gunners and a few Humber Light Recce Cars apparently in Australian service, they were incorporated into Blackforce, under Brigadier A S Black-burn VC, who had gained his award at Pozière on the Somme in 1916. By 8 March Java, too, was untenable and on orders from General Sitwell the tanks were dumped into a deep ravine. While a number of British armoured regiments served with the Indian forces in Burma an Indian armoured division was based in the Levant and some famous Indian cavalry regiments, equipped with armoured cars, supported Indian infantry divisions in Italy.

There has been a tendency in post-war accounts of the fighting in Burma to refer to the M3 Medium tanks in that theatre as Lee/Grants. If one is prepared to accept the evidence of surviving photographs as conclusive, then it would seem that they were almost all Lees, modified slightly to suit British tastes. This simply involving the commander's machine-gun cupola from the turret, replacing it with a flush fitting hatch and mounting an external smoke discharger at the side. However, such vague terminology is hardly justified, since a good deal of information exists in the unit war diaries. The picture they reveal is by no means crystal clear, but since it has never been recorded before there is some justification for including it here, especially since it also throws up a number of other interesting sidelights on armoured warfare in a theatre that has not received its full share of attention.

Of the eleven British armoured regiments operating in India and fighting in Burma during the war, one was regular cavalry, two were cavalry regiments formed during the war, and the other eight all converted to armour from infantry battalions. Starting with the these last, 116th RAC (the erstwhile 9th Battalion, the Gordon Highlanders) presents a typical case. Their war diary is not very encouraging to begin with. It records that between October 1942 and May 1943 they received a total of fifty-two M3 Medium Grants or Lees. Does one read that as an admission that they didn't know the difference, or did they mean they got some of each? They appear to have been on constant exercises in various parts of India for the next ten months without any recorded change of equipment, but in March 1944 they received their first Shermans, one of which was identified as an M4A4. Further

searching reveals a Parade State return for 1 April which explains matters. At this time the regiment had seventeen Shermans, eighteen Lees and seventeen Grants, along with ten turretless Stuarts. A few more Shermans arrived in May and June while thirteen of their Grants were returned to Secunderabad, leaving them with just about enough medium tanks to equip three squadrons. Knowing how popular turretless Stuarts became in all theatres, the entry for 28 June 1944 is quite surprising. It records delivery of eleven Stuart turrets and the same number of 37-mm guns. Clearly if they wanted turreted Stuarts they would have to make them for themselves.

In its war diary, 146 RAC (9th Battalion the Duke of Wellington's Regiment) records having Valentines, along with an armoured car troop equipped with Ford armoured cars (presumably Indian Pattern Carriers) in October 1942. A month later they received six Universal Carriers which were allocated to their mortar platoon, and referred again to their armoured car troop in January 1943. They made a point of recording the arrival of three Valentines with three-man turrets in February 1943; they were the only regiment to take gun-equipped Valentines into action in this theatre. Eight tanks from C Squadron were shipped across the Bay of Bengal from India to the Arakan on the Burmese coast, to be used against a strong Japanese position at Donbiak, but the conditions were appalling and eight tanks were simply not enough to undertake the

63   Valentines of 146 RAC, one on a White/Ruxtall transporter, at the time of the Donbiak action.

task. The Japanese had incorporated some captured British 2-pounder anti-tank guns into their defences and the regiment was pleased to note that the tanks were virtually immune to them, even at close range. However three of the tanks, complete with their crews, were lost in rather mysterious circumstances. In October 1944 the war diary is speaking of Grants, which were starting to arrive, as operational tanks while the remaining Valentines were referred to as training tanks. Shortly afterwards the regiment was told that C Squadron 'will have to have Lee tanks in place of Grants as there were insufficient of the latter in the country ' – a statement that could be taken to mean that the Grant was regarded as the ideal tank; after all, it was the British version, and the Lee very much second best. In February 1945, 146 RAC got its revenge for Donbiak. A Squadron was earmarked for 'Operation Turret' the assault on Ramree Island, which proved successful. When the area around Donbiak was cleared the three missing Valentines from the 1943 battle were discovered where they had plunged into a hidden ditch, along with the remains of five crew members. Starting in May 1945 the regiment began to convert to Shermans.

The 149 RAC (7th Battalion, King's Own Yorkshire Light Infantry) were reasonably specific about their tanks. Their war diary mentions that C Squadron had 'I' (or Infantry) tanks in March 1943, which must be assumed to have been Valentines, but in July 1943 they claimed to have one squadron of Shermans while the remaining tanks in the regiment were described as Grants. For 150 RAC (10th Battalion, York and Lancaster Regiment) the records are not so complete. They had Valentines in December 1941 but they seemed to have changed to Lees early in the following year. One entry of note is dated 28 March 1944, concerning a signal emanating from IVXth Army which instructed them to remove the cupolas from all Lee tanks before they were despatched. The same signal cannot be found in any other war diary, so it is impossible to say for certain that this was a sudden decision implemented all round. Since the instruction preceded a movement by rail it is just possible that it was required in order to reduce the height of the tanks, but it seems more reasonable to assume that it was done for operational reasons. Removing the turret cupola from a Lee reduced the overall height by about 7 in. and it is interesting to note that where this information is given on a Department of Tank Design loading diagram dated June 1944, it is annotated 'vehicle ex-UK (without cupola)'.

The next three regiments all have very similar accounts. The 158 RAC (9th Battalion, South Wales Borderers) was formed in Britain and equipped with three Grants when it was based at Southend. In India, on 20 December 1942, they had twenty-three Grants and seven Stuarts. They received eleven more Grants in January 1943 but in February they passed ten Grants to the 26th Hussars and ten Stuarts to 25th Dragoons. At the same time they obtained nineteen wheeled carriers. The beginnings of 159

RAC (10th Battalion, the Gloucestershire Regiment) were identical but their first return from India, dated 29 December 1942, listed thirty-seven Lees and seven Stuarts. By the end of February they had only eleven Lees left, and a month later none, at which stage they reverted to infantry. The last of this group for which records are available is 160 RAC (12th Battalion, the Green Howards). Again they started out in Essex with three Grants, but had nothing at all to say about the tanks taken over in India. The war diary of 163 RAC (13th Battalion, the Sherwood Foresters) never mentions tanks at all!

If the early state of tank availability in India needs emphasing, then the place to look is the war diary of the 25th Dragoons. In April 1941 they were issued with fourteen Morris-Commercial six-wheeled ambulances and by July these had been replaced by hired lorries and what were described as derelict buses. Matters were not made any better by the complaint that, upon formation, they had had dumped upon them all the undesirable rejects from other regiments. These people generally proved to be poor soldiers, with very little mechanical apptitude, and it cannot have helped that they had to start their careers as tank crews in so many old buses. A few pre-war light tanks began to trickle through from August, and in October 1942 they reported the arrival of fifteen armoured cars, although their disgust was evidently such that they did not even bother to record what type these were. Conversely, when tanks did start to arrive, from November 1942 onwards, there is great detail. They received sixteen Valentine Mark Vs on the 8th, and eight more on the 27th. A further sixteen were delivered in December, along with eleven Valentine Mark IIs and two Mark IIIs, which at least gives some idea of the variety of Valentines dispatched to that country. By March 1943 they had re-equipped with Stuarts, a mixture of Mark I Hybrid and M3A1 Stuart IIIs. Four Canadian Scout Cars (Lynx) arrived in July 1943 and from August they started converting to Lees. Following their withdrawal from Burma the regiment temporarily reverted to Valentines plus six Sherman OP tanks, but between November 1944 and January 1945 converted to Shermans of the M4A2 diesel type. As the war drew to a close they were commencing to train in Sherman DD tanks.

Starting a little later than the 25th Dragoons, the 26th Hussars actually had some Light Tanks Mark IIB and even an ancient Crossley armoured car at the outset. They got a couple of Light Mark IVA tanks a month later, and the first mention of Grants in the war diary is in September 1942. From then on things got complicated. Five Lees arrived in October 1942 along with fifteen armoured cars. However, when they gave a demonstration to the infantry in October they were able to show a Grant, a Lee, a Stuart and an Indian Pattern Wheeled Carrier – one of the anonymous armoured cars? They supplied eleven Grants to 158 RAC in December 1942 and got ten back from them two months later. A month after that the same regiment

64 *A Lee in Burma, mounting the long 75-mm gun. It has a Grant style hatch and British pattern smoke discharger on the turret.*

sent them twenty Grants and four Lees. They also received four Lynx scout cars in July 1943, but were disbanded in the October.

Finally the regular regiment, 3rd Carabiniers. When the war in Europe began they were in India, equipped with Indian Pattern Light Mark VIB tanks. Events in the West precluded any immediate change and it was not until November 1941 that they started to receive some Stuarts. They were told that their new establishment would be one light and two medium squadrons, but almost at once this was changed to three medium squadrons, although there were very few actual tanks. By May 1942 they could field three Grants, seven Lees and three Stuarts but in July they were instructed to release all their Grants and Lees for the Middle East. No other regiment records this instruction and although the Carabiniers lost the few medium tanks they had at this time, it is by no means certain that any were shipped back to Egypt. Later that year they could muster a selection of Grants, Lees and Stuarts again, but by February 1943 they had reverted entirely to Stuarts. In June they were informed that theirs was to be an infantry tank role for which, at the very least, one might expect

Grants or Lees, but instead they retained their Stuarts: forty-two of the Mark I Hybrid and ten Mark III (M3A1). Lees replaced the Stuarts in July, and with these they began a brilliant combat career in Burma. While it may not be typical, photographs of 3rd Carabiniers Lees in Burma show at least some of them with a sort of lifeline looped around the turret, presumably for infantry passengers to hang on to.

If this long and possibly rather tedious account proves anything, then it seems to show that in India, at any rate, there were almost as many Grants as Lees. If, as seems reasonable, one can assume that Grants were preferred, then it is strange to see that the two types were issued so indiscriminately for active service. There would be Lees fighting in Burma, while Grants remained with regiments training in India. It also serves to show just what it was like being at the farthest end of the supply line. Similar tales could be told of the indigenous Indian regiments. Seven regiments of the Indian Armoured Corps were brigaded with those British units already mentioned and took an active part in the campaign in Burma, equipped with the same types of tanks.

65   *The Valentine Burmark during a demonstration in Britain.*

When the tide turned against the Japanese in Burma, and the advance on Rangoon began, armour played an important part in the victory. Yet it was hardly tank warfare as practised on Salisbury Plain. For one thing, the Japanese showed little aptitude for tank fighting and most of their tanks were inferior even to the Stuarts of regiments such as the Indian 7th Light Cavalry. Where the Japanese excelled, when it wasn't suicidal attacks, was in tenacious defence and they devised deep and intricate bunker complexes which could not be taken by direct infantry assault without dreadful losses. The tanks had already learned the advantage of intimate support from the foot soldiers, and many worked in such harmony that they were virtually inseparable. This teamwork was the key to bunker-busting. Following an artillery barrage the attack went in, with tanks firing high explosive to blow away any vegetation that masked the firing slits. Now the infantry closed in while the tanks, depending on the acknowledged accuracy of their 75-mm guns, fired armour-piercing rounds through the bunker walls just below the firing slits. Once the immediate opposition had been suppressed, delayed-action high-explosive was fired to bring the bunkers down, or smoke which, drifting along the hidden passages, would seep out from otherwise unidentified slits which could then be taken out.

Specialised armour did not play a significant part in the fighting for Burma. One of the British regiments developed and demonstrated two unusual devices which could be attached to Grants for clearing mines but few details survive and the only equipment to see active service was the Valentine bridgelayer, of which six were operating in the theatre, while some Valentine DDs were used for

training in India. The arrival of 401 Independent Scorpion Squadron has already been mentioned. That they had turreted Grant Scorpions by November 1944 is clear from a mention of 37-mm gun training, but which mark they were is not recorded. Sherman DDs and Grant CDL tanks arrived just as the conflict was ending, but the things that demand our interest are those developed especially with Far Eastern service in mind. One such was Burmark: as its name implies, an ARK for use in Burma. Built on a turretless Valentine hull, it was much lighter than the Churchill variants employed in Europe.

66   *The Topee attachment on a Sherman DD. The armoured panels that would normally enclose the top of the folded screen are hanging downwards and, as a further refinement, two remote control .30 Brownings have been fitted which will rise with the screen.*

Topee was the name given to a system for protecting deflated DD tank screens. Although it was invented by the Amphibious Trials and Development Centre in England, this was clearly done with jungle conditions in mind since its stated purpose was to protect the screen – not just against small-arms fire – but also from tearing on low branches and undergrowth. All around the base of the screen was a series of 6-mm bullet-proof panels, hinged half way up so that when the screen was lowered the top plate lay across it to give overhead protection. When the screen was raised the hinged plate drop outwards and was clamped to its lower half, providing 12 mm protection to the lowest part of the flotation screen. According to a contemporary report there was no adverse effect on the performance of the DD. Topee came in two versions. Mark I fitted the original DD only, while Mark II would also fit the improved Mark II DD and, it was hoped, the American-built Mark III DD as well. Problems were experienced in launching from some types of landing craft, but in general the equipment looked promising and might have been adopted had the war continued.

Tank-mounted flamethrowers were a very desirable weapon for service in Burma but it was agreed that the Crocodile type would be unsuitable, on account of its trailer. Discussions at first centred on a light tank version, but this was turned down by the General Staff who pointed out that a light tank was too thinly armoured for use with such a short-range weapon. Interest then switched to a design called Salamander. A wooden mock-up based on the Sherman was first developed, early in 1944, although the Churchill was also being considered. A fuel capacity of 200 gallons was specified and, since there was not room for both, it was agreed that the flame projector would replace the main armament in the turret. This was the downfall of the whole project, since it proved impossible to create a totally leakproof rotary junction in the turret base, which is the last place one needs petrol or even petrol fumes wafting about. Lagonda Ltd, of London then set about the design of an externally mounted flame-thrower system which, as Adder, would fit the Sherman V (M4A4), and as Cobra the Churchill. It consisted of a rear-mounted 80-gallon fuel tank under 14 mm of armour, a protected pipe leading down the side of the hull to a projector mounted as close as possible to the co-driver's position, since he would be the operator. Inert gas propellant would be employed until a suitable cordite system could be developed. Adder had an effective range of 100 yards. It seems that the Cobra project was soon dropped, because no orders were placed, but 350 Adder units were ordered and they were designed in such a way that the entire kit could be supplied to regimental Light Aid Detachments for fitting in the field, the scale of issue being nine per regiment to those equipped with Shermans in South East Asia Command. Fifteen had been produced by the end of May 1945 and a further order for 150 units, modified to fit the Sherman III (M4A2) was then received.

67 A Sherman Adder flamethrower. Viewed from this side it is possible to see the fuel tank at the back, the armoured cover along the hull top and the projector, in the hull gunner's hatch. The 6-mm thick armoured skirting plates were not specifically designed for the Adder. This tank also had an American Direct Vision Cupola fitted.

Again, however, they appear to have arrived too late to see active service.

Rangoon fell to an assault from the sea early in May 1945 while General Slim's Fourteenth Army, advancing on two parallel fronts, was still 100 miles or more short of the city, but it was a close thing. Undoubtedly the speed of their advance was due in no small part to the presence of armour: Stuarts, Grants, Lees and an increasing number of Shermans, employed with courage and consummate skill in a country many had believed quite unsuitable for tanks. Yet if this had been the view with regard to the mainland, how much more might it have applied to the Pacific islands?

Of the Commonwealth forces in the South Pacific, it was the Australians who first employed tanks – Stuarts, on Papua New Guinea in December 1942. As with the campaign in Burma, their use was mainly in the role of bunker-busting, but the conditions were atrocious and experience at first severely limited since the regiment, 2/6 Armoured, had been trained for North African conditions. Even short tactical moves often had to be made by sea, under constant threat of air attack, and when they were ashore the tanks had to operate with great care over treacherous, swampy ground. From October 1943 the Australians had Matildas operating in New Guinea, and in doing so discovered the ideal tank for this kind of warfare – the infantry tank doing what it was designed for. At this time the Japanese had no anti-tank weapon that could do more than scratch it, and as long as the ground was chosen carefully the Matilda could move close up to a bunker and obliterate it. Matildas may have been outclassed in the Northern Hemisphere, but the Australian Army employed them right up to the end of the war on Wewak, Bougainville and in Borneo with great success.

By July 1944, however, the tank situation in Australia was grim. Army Headquarters in Melbourne estimated that they had access to enough spares to keep 100 Matildas running for six months, based on a training schedule of eight hours running per week, but if they were expected to go on active service the situation would deteriorate fast, and the position with Grants was little better. For their tank brigades the Australians favoured Churchills, but found it less easy to decide on the armoured divisions. The obvious answer was Shermans, but since these were already destined to be replaced by the T26 perhaps that would be better, or the new British A34 Comet or even A41. Since the Churchill was already chosen the Australian government lodged a bid for 310, which included six for training and 130 in reserve, specifying the new Marks VII and VIII. To begin with they wondered if the War Office in London would agree to deliver 100 by February 1945 in order that one tank brigade might be equipped, but it was rather a forlorn hope. In a mood of almost unreal optimism the War Office considered a scenario where the war against Germany was over by 1 October 1944 – and remember, this is July 1944. In that unlikely event they would first equip two British tank brigades with Churchills for service in the Far East and then consider Australia's needs. It was reckoned that seventeen Mark VIIIs would go in December, 100 Mark VIIs in June 1945, and the remainder over the following two months. If the European war ended on 1 January 1945 the timetable would be little different except for the December delivery, but no forecast was offered if, as it did, the war went on until May. In the event, no Churchills were committed to the Far East, although Australia finally received one regiment's worth (fifty-one tanks) just too late to use them. The Australian Army also expressed

an interest in Churchill-based specialised armour and it is interesting to note that their surviving Crocodile flamethrower, preserved in the Royal Australian Armoured Corps Museum at Puckapunyal, is a Mark VIII version mounting the 95-mm howitzer, which in many respects would seem to be a more sensible arrangement than the British Mark VII combination.

The Australian Cruiser tank, the Sentinel, never had a chance to test its mettle against a real enemy. Even so, development continued. As explained in the earlier volume of this work, there never was a Mark 2, but a Mark 3 appeared in mid-1943 which, with the Pacific campaign in mind, had a most intelligent choice of main armament; the Australian-produced version of the 25-pounder gun. The hull was slightly reshaped and the hull machine-gun position eliminated, while the turret ring diameter was

69   *The experimental 17-pounder turret mounted on a stripped AC1 Sentinel hull, seen here running with the turret reversed.*

68   *A side view of the AC3 prototype showing the thicker barrel of the 25-pounder gun and extra side-stowage lockers.*

enlarged to accept a bigger turret. Since British and American tanks were now being delivered in sufficient numbers the Australian Cruiser programme was cut back and the AC3 never went into production. One hull was later used to mount a 17-pounder turret on an even larger turret ring, but before this was done, in order to see if it would withstand the recoil, a special trial turret was fitted with the awe-inspiring combination of twin 25-pounders which were fired simultaneously. From the AC3 design onwards, with the elimination of the hull weapon, the crew was reduced from five to four, but even so the weight increased and in an effort to match this with adequate power a combination of four Gipsy Major (Tiger Moth) engines was tried in place of the triple Perrier-Cadillac installation. Although, from a combat point of view, the Australian Cruiser will always remain an unknown quantity, it is worth emphasising that its production, in a country where no tank had ever been built before, was no mean achievement. Further, to discover that the basic design had sufficient stretch potential to be upgunned twice in little over two years is nothing less than astounding. Would it be too invidious to point out that such a jump, from 2-pounder, through 25-pounder to 17-pounder, was beyond the capabilities of any contemporary British tank except, in the last two stages, as a self-propelled gun?

Past masters at improvisation, the Australians also developed their own family of specialised armoured vehicles, which they dubbed Circus Equipment. It included bulldozing versions of the Grant and Matilda, and a flamethrowing variant of the Matilda called Frog. Early experiments were disappointing, but in its final form, with the flame projector replacing the 2-pounder in the turret, it proved a most effective weapon, with a fuel capacity of 225 gallons and a range of 80 yards. Some were used operationally in Borneo. However, the most devastating weapon, developed specifically for bunker-busting, was the Hedgehog. The original idea was to fit a tank with a naval-pattern depth charge launcher, but when this proved impossible another anti-submarine weapon, the Hedgehog, was selected instead. Seven of the bombs were installed in a box-shaped launcher hinged to the rear deck of the tank. Folded down for normal running, the box was elevated as the tank approached its target, and the six missiles launched high over the turret to land about 200 yards ahead. Pin-point accuracy might not have been guaranteed, but any target thus straddled must have been obliterated, not to mention the morale effect.

What the Australians achieved with tanks they could not match with wheeled vehicles. Their own Dingo Scout Car could not be compared in any way with the British Daimler, being chronically uncomfortable to drive, and very large for its purpose, while its bigger counterpart was the even uglier Rover. Classed officially as a Light Armoured Car, just over ninety were built in three batches on locally assembled Canadian Ford 3-tonner chassis of two different wheelbase lengths. This meant that the first

70 An Australian Matilda Frog giving a suitably relaxed flamethrower demonstration in Borneo in 1945.

71 A Rover light armoured car with its wire mesh roof panels unfolded.

72 The big Rhino armoured car with its Crusader-style turret. Notice the tyre chains stowed on the hull, and the circular escape hatch.

forty or so were just over 20 ft long, while the remainder were 18 ft 6 in., which must have played havoc with maintenance schedules. The chassis was four-wheel drive, of course, but considering the shape of the vehicle, it is surprising to discover that it was of front-engine layout. The driver and an observer sat either side of the engine in a front compartment which had folding armour panels for a roof, and a bulkhead with an opening in it leading back to the fighting compartment. Here three more crew members were located in a large, rectangular body which had hinged wire-mesh covers, intended, the handbook explains, to keep out hand grenades and the enemy. There was no turret, nor even fixed weapons, but the Rover had six optional mountings for machine-guns. One, at the front, would accept a Bren or Vickers gun that was fired by the observer, while those in the back comprised one on each side, another pointing rearwards and two anti-aircraft positions at each end of the fighting compartment. The hull was built from 8-mm armour plate; it was extremely well shaped to compensate, yet it is difficult to justify the title of armoured car. It appears to have had much more in common with the Indian Wheeled Carriers, although one Australian commentator described it rather unkindly as a mobile slit trench, which is probably nearer the truth. A more conventional armoured car, known as the Rhino, appeared in prototype form in 1943. It was a 7.5-ton vehicle, powered by a rear-mounted Chevrolet engine on a four-wheel drive GMC chassis. The hull was well shaped, with 30-mm armour at the front and, rather surprisingly, at the back as well, but it was an ungainly looking vehicle. The turret, which was rather Crusader shaped, mounted a 2-pounder gun and coaxial Vickers, only added to the top-heavy appearance that must have been even more apparent when the car was travelling at its top speed of 45 mph. Australia took delivery of a few AEC Dorchester armoured command vehicles, and also produced a home-designed prototype on a six-wheel drive Ford/Marmon-Herrington chassis, but their most successful wheeled AFV was a simple armoured utility car which was supplied in limited numbers to US forces in the Pacific theatre.

What the Matilda was to the Australians in the Pacific, the Valentine was to the New Zealand Army. Thirty were delivered starting in October 1941, and further deliveries through 1942 brought the total up to around 250, all of the 2-pounder variety. Since there was no close support version of the Valentine, thirty-three Matilda Mark IVCS were acquired and the light tank requirement was made up with some 300 Stuarts. These last proved to be something of a disaster, being the bastard M3 with M3A1 turret

73 *The Australian-designed armoured command vehicle.*

version, which gave every appearance of having been thrown together in a hurry. Polite to a fault, the New Zealanders accepted the name Stuart Hybrid for them, and then expended a great deal of ingenuity turning them into combat worthy tanks. In the meantime it had been decided to raise a tank squadron for active service on Guadalcanal, and it was agreed that in order to avoid a spares nightmare only AEC-engined Valentines would be employed. This, of course, robbed the unit immediately of its close support tanks and to overcome this it was necessary to exercise even more ingenuity. A number of 3-in. howitzers from Matildas were transferred to some of the Valentines. There was nothing inherently difficult in this, because the howitzer and 2-pounder were effectively interchangeable in most other British tanks. Such problems as there were involved modifications to the sighting telescope, which were first worked out on a trial and error basis and then remounted to suit. Schemes were also devised to produce a high-explosive round for the 2-pounder, using Bofors 40-mm or US 37-mm shells.

The only other AFV assembled in New Zealand, besides those dealt with in *The Great Tank Scandal*, was a version of the Indian Wheeled Carrier Mark II. It seems that the original plan was to construct them for the Indian government using imported Canadian Ford, rear-engined, four-wheel drive chassis and armour plate shipped in from the United States. When the demand from India did not materialise a small number were built for home defence duties, but they were never considered impressive examples of armoured vehicle design, especially in view of the wooden fighting compartment floors, which would have been very vulnerable to mine blast.

5 The American saga

74 *An imported Cromwell, posed for its official recognition photographs at Aberdeen Proving Ground, Maryland, in 1944.*

Shortly before Christmas 1942 Michael Dewar, head of the British Tank Mission in Washington, learned that he was to be replaced. The news was brought to him by Sir William Rootes and Sir Walter Venning, who were in the United States as part of a visiting tank engine mission headed by Miles Thomas of Nuffields, as yet unknighted. Rootes told Dewar that in future, policy demanded that tank procurement in the USA was to be an all-military affair. Dewar's diary suggests that he took the news more in anger than sorrow. In his own view, he had led matters to a stage from which they could only improve. Indeed he saw himself and his team as a motivating force in the design and adoption of the Sherman tank, and he had made many useful friends for Britain in his time, which was no doubt one reason why he was awarded the American Medal of Merit on 1 March 1943.

The Tank Engine Mission was in the United States to see what was available for British tanks. It was a mixed team of industrialists and military men who, after a brief stop-over in Washington, made straight for Detroit, where the hardware was actually produced. Detroit was separated from Washington by more than just miles. The tough business men in the automobile capital, one of whom was a retired U-boat commander from the First World War, were a world away from the political and military hierarchy at the seat of government, and they were trained to sell. Most were already fully committed to the American tank programme, although Packard, who were building the Rolls-Royce Merlin for the Royal Air Force, reckoned they had production capacity to spare. But the real hard-sell came from Ford Motors, who were backed by the authorities in Washington.

Ford had designed a V12 aero-engine from which they developed a V8 that, they hoped, could be made to deliver 500 hp as a tank power unit. In fact they were also attempting to build a tank version of the V12 at their Lincoln plant, which was rejected by the British team at that stage because of its undeveloped state. America intended to standardise on the Ford V8 and promoted it heavily against the Meteor on the grounds of Allied compatibility. Roy Robotham, who had seen it earlier in the year, had his doubts. It was only two-thirds the size of his Meteor and he could not see how it could ever be made to produce 500 hp in any consistent way under armour. The Tank Engine Mission seemed sold on the idea, however, and agreed, in the interests of standardisation, to recommend that Morris and Leyland in Britain should build the Ford engine in preference to the Meteor. (That, at least, was the official line. In his autobiography,* Sir Miles Thomas claims that when he came home he advised Sir Andrew Duncan in favour of the Meteor, which seems very strange in view of his recent advocacy, recorded above, for the Cavalier against the Centaur. Did he do this behind Lord Nuffield's back?)

In Britain their advice was taken seriously enough for seven tanks to be shipped across to the USA. These were one complete Cromwell and six engineless Centaur hulls, four of which would be fitted with Ford V8s and two with

*Sir M Thomas, *Out on a Wing*, Michael Joseph, 1964.

the promised V12 once it was ready. In April a report from the USA stated that production difficulties with the V8 now suggested a maximum power output of 400–450 hp, causing the Tank Board, on 18 May 1943, to declare that the Ford did not compare, powerwise, with the Meteor or even the Liberty. Concerning this last engine it is worth a brief digression to record another statement from Sir Miles Thomas in his autobiography. Regarding the troubled history of this power unit in the Crusader, he explained that the problem was due entirely to the method of construction. Being of First World War vintage, and designed for use in aircraft, it consisted of individual pairs of cylinders joined together, unlike the more modern Meteor, for instance, in which the cylinder block was a single casting. In an aircraft this form of construction was fine, but in a tank, as Sir Miles explained, it was subject to so many vicious blows and stresses that the cylinders gradually worked apart and, in doing so, warped the crankcase, causing oil gallery fractures and leaks, with which tank crews in the desert were only too familiar. One wonders when he first discovered this?

The tale of the British cruiser tanks in America can be dealt with quickly by reference to a letter, dated 15 October 1943, from Major General Alec Richardson of the British Army Staff in Washington to General Raymond Briggs, Director, Royal Armoured Corps (DRAC) in Britain; a source which will be drawn on again in this chapter:

> These tanks have made us a laughing stock out here. The Cromwell has had a variety of troubles, and it was mad only sending out . . . one. The Americans are politely indifferent to what happens to them, and Waller, the Rolls-Royce man with them, is *most* unhappy and wants them withdrawn as soon as possible. We are undoubtedly the world's worst salesmen!
>
> We have lost a lot of prestige over these poor lone derelicts.

WE MUST REGAIN OUR PRESTIGE.

Earlier in his letter Richardson refers to the Lucas Mission that was then in the United States, and this raises another interesting point. The British Tank Board minutes contain a paraphrase of a Secret incoming telegram from Averall Harriman, one of President Roosevelt's special advisors, to Colonel George Green, his representative in London, dated 2 September 1943. In this he quotes the US General Somervell, a good friend of the British in Washington, who claims that they (the Americans) are anxious for a British Tank Mission to visit the States but wish it to be headed by a senior man 'and not repeat not Lucas'.

Oliver Lucas, as his name suggests, was the third generation managing director of the family business which supplied lights and other electrical components for motor cars. He held the post of Director of Tank Design during the war but is described in a biographical essay as 'sarcastic to the point of rudeness . . . an autocrat who did not have the common touch' and 'passionately pro-British'.

Enough reasons, one supposes, to turn the entire population of the United States against him. Yet, it seems, he headed that mission of which Richardson says 'no one knows what they are really out here for'. This is probably as good an example as any of an attitude held by many politicians, soldiers and civil servants in Britain, an attitude regularly bewailed by Britain's representatives in the United States, and which to the Americans smacked of patronising arrogance that could be little justified and ill-afforded.

Returning, for a moment, to the Ford-engined Centaurs, a Fighting Vehicle Proving Establishment report issued towards the end of 1944 remarks that it was a much more flexible power unit than the Liberty. This was indicated by the fact that the driver did not need to do anything like so much gear-changing and therefore found his task less tiring.

Visiting missions might come and go, but it was to the permanent British staff in Washington and Detroit that the real work fell. Douglas Pratt replaced Michael Dewar in Washington, but Brigadier MacLeod Ross remained in Detroit, despite being a Lucas nominee. Although participants such as Robotham and Miles Thomas left brief accounts of their involvement with tanks in their autobiographies, and the views of many military men can be found in official files, only MacLeod Ross wrote a complete book about it. *The Business of Tanks* is a curious work. Despite some bias, it is fair enough in most of its criticisms of British tank design, but then goes completely overboard in favour of American practices, at least on the production side; it may not be irrelevant to remark that the author chose to settle in North America after the war. In the letter already partly quoted above from Richardson to Briggs, the former makes two interesting comments:

> I advise you to be very careful as to the amount of faith you put into the Tank Automotive Center Technical Summaries. Ross seems to have led us up the garden and I fear that Tony Bouchier may do the same.

Colonel Bouchier RTR, was MacLeod Ross' deputy in Detroit and the pair of them issued the technical summaries for consumption in Britain. Further into his letter Richardson says:

> I think Tony B. and Ross are both technical wafflers, and rather a menace, as they carry too much weight technically and the result is we get nowhere. They talk a hell of a lot and spread a sort of technical (semi) cobweb over everything which clouds the issue and prevents Alec Gatehouse getting a clear picture.

What the Americans thought is not so easy to discover, although they clearly could not stand Oliver Lucas, but the general impression is that the people they were really prepared to listen to were experienced combat soldiers straight out of the Western Desert – men like Alec Gatehouse, who had commanded 10th Armoured Division, George Witheridge and J N Berkeley Miller.

When all the sniping and back-biting is put aside, it is clear that none of the British representatives in the United States had an easy task. It is all too easy to become dazzled by statistics where mass production is concerned, but it is worth recalling that the Sherman tank, as a concept, had first been proposed in August 1940 and that it was two years later before production began. Even that was only the start, for true mass production takes a while to get into its stride and is continually bedevilled by minor changes and retrospective modifications. The result, as the British had already discovered, was that most tanks were out of date ere they entered service, and to some extent the Sherman was no exception.

Richardson made some observations late in 1943 that had a bearing on this. Even at that date, he noted, public opinion in the United States regarded the war in Europe as all but won – and this more than six months before D-Day! This sentiment, in turn, had repercussions in Detroit where the industrialists, steeped in economic reality, felt the need to reduce the scale of tank production lest the market be swamped, knowing that the juggernaut would take a lot of stopping. A cynic might feel that it was this threat of over-production that lay behind an astounding offer which the British Army Staff in Washington forwarded to London on 29 March 1943. Indeed, our cynic could have placed other untoward interpretations upon it, but for the fact that it emanated from General Somervell who, one feels, was above such deviousness, and in any case it made a good deal of sense. The gist of it was that before Cromwell production got into its stride the entire programme should be cancelled and the shortfall of 4,000-odd tanks made up with Shermans since, as Somervell pointed out, the two tanks, Cromwell and Sherman, were similar enough to be interchangeable in British regiments. Somervell explained that what he called the Russian Protocol had changed and that this would require a cutback in Sherman production which could affect Britain if the Cromwell failed to come up to expectations. If the British argued that shipping capacity was limited, and there was no point in settling entirely for Shermans if they remained nose-to-tail on the dockside in US ports, Somervell countered that this shipping space could be found by reducing orders for heavy construction and railroad equipment. In essence, Somervell was suggesting that Britain should stop building a range of cruiser tanks which, in American eyes, were not much good anyway, and concentrate on heavy plant and railway locomotives that it was renowned for. Such material formed about one-third of all equipment shipped across the Atlantic in 1943, and most of it was very awkward to handle as cargo. Thus in many respects Somervell's offer made a great deal of sense. Let it be understood that there was no suggestion of Britain giving up tank production altogether. Nothing was said about abandoning the Churchill or long-term plans for a new generation of tanks; this was an expedient and mutually advantageous step for the immediate future. The British response, delivered on 9 April 1943, was polite but firm. It was deemed a matter of 'high policy' that Britain should continue to produce tanks; they could not agree to this 'complete dependency', suggesting that the War Office had placed a darker interpretation on the offer than was perhaps intended. Further, it was pointed out, British requirements were also reducing, to around 3,000 in the case of Cromwells, but there was still a considerable need for Sherman spare parts. Thus, for this and other reasons, Sherman production was scaled down, with the result that by late 1944 the US Army found itself running desperately short of tanks, just as Britain had done in 1940.

The Sherman, as an apparently standardised product, is often pointed to as an intelligent contrast to the great variety of British tanks, but that standardisation was by no means total. In addition to the obvious difference between cast and welded hulls, there were four major engine variants requiring quite different hull arrangements which did not permit interchangeability. Thus it made sense, as far as possible, to distribute the different models separately. Everyone got their share of the radial-engined M4 and M4A1 but, since they ran much of their tank army on diesel fuel, it made sense that the Russians should be supplied mainly with the M4A2 model. The United States effectively sold itself the Ford V8 and took the M4A3, while Britain selected, or more probably was left with the M4A4. This was the version that sported a Chrysler A57 Multibank engine. This amazing creation was, in fact, a cluster of five Chrysler six-cylinder water-cooled engines, forming a power unit of prodigious size and complexity which, despite having a total of thirty cylinders, only developed 425 hp. To visitors like Robotham of Rolls-Royce, it was regarded with unmixed horror, and few Britons had anything good to say for it on first acquaintance, while the Americans declared that they would not employ the M4A4 on overseas service at all. This is no different, in essence, from the British statement of unbattleworthiness applied to the Covenanter. Even so, Britain took most of the 7,500 M4A4s built before production ceased in September 1943 (including 1,400 originally allocated to the US Army for training) and found them to be quite serviceable if one overlooked maintenance difficulties. Indeed it probably accorded well with the British temperament to make a virtue from trying to get the best out of the worst possible engine.

Another common problem was the link between tank and gun, or rather the apparent lack of any link. While the Tank Automotive Center in Detroit took care of the armoured vehicle, its fighting capability was decided by the Ordnance Board in Washington, and therein lay further potential problems. It was quite clear, when the Sherman was designed, that it would have to be upgunned in due course, and the system of bolting the mantlet to the turret was evolved with this in mind. By the summer of 1942 the Ordnance Board had selected a 76.2-mm gun, generally known as the 76-mm, although it was an awkward fit in the standard Sherman turret. By August 1943 Britain had agreed to take as many 76-mm gun Shermans as it could get, although it was understood that the design of a new turret to take it was not yet finalised. By December it was announced that 2,000 76-mm gun Shermans on an M4A1 hull (then designated M4E6) had been earmarked for Britain although, in the event, few were supplied since something better came along. A close support version of the Sherman, mounting a 105-mm howitzer, was also developed in the United States and Britain was looking at M4A1 and M4A3 versions of this, but again only appears to have taken a few.

The light tank situation was no less complicated. British requirements for the 37-mm gun Stuart series were dwindling fast, and could probably all have been met by deliveries of the M3A3 (Stuart V) version. However, in the

United States development had continued with the Cadillac-powered M5 series. Having examined the new tank a British officer described it as of pepperpot appearance, an effect probably created by the enlarged engine compartment, and it was further remarked that Cadillac workmanship was simply too good for such a tank. Three of the improved M5A1 model were due in Britain for evaluation in July 1943, and both types were accepted for service as the Stuart VI. Cadillac later found a more suitable product to match their status in the T24, which first appeared in October 1943. This superb machine retained the engine and transmission layout of the M5A1 but employed torsion bar suspension and mounted a 75-mm weapon, modified from an aircraft cannon. The hull and turret form was a vast improvement on the earlier, more upright designs developed in the USA and it is worth noting that this was achieved with the old configuration of rear engines and front transmission. Britain placed an urgent order for six, for evaluation, on 30 December 1943. On entering production the tank was classified M24 and a few were made available to the British in the last months of the war. Known as the Chaffee (a name which the Americans subsequently adopted) it was reported that upon delivery they were only stowed for four, although it was planned to modify them to suit a five-man crew before issue to service units.

America's counterpart of the Tetrarch was the Light Tank T9, although it was designed from the outset as an air-portable light tank. The project was handled by Marmon-Herrington in Indianapolis and the result was a tiny, three-man machine weighing seven tons and armed with a 37-mm gun and coaxial Browning. Since delivery by glider was not considered, the project centred around the Douglas C54A Skymaster, a military version of the four-engined DC4 airliner.

In order to carry the tank it was first necessary to remove the turret. With the tank parked alongside the aircraft, this was lifted off by hoists mounted above the

75 An M5A1 (Stuart VI) in British service showing the raised rear engine deck and enlarged turret.

76 A pair of M24 Chaffees leading two columns of Cromwells at a parade.

77　A Locust light tank of 6th Airborne Recce Regiment in front of a General Aircraft Hamilcar glider.

aircraft's loading hatch. The turret was then swung inside the plane, while the hull was driven round and positioned beneath the fuselage, between the wings, close to the centre of gravity. A four-point hoist beneath the fuselage then lifted the tank until it made contact with the underside of the plane, where four spring locks engaged with lugs provided on the tank's hull. Trials revealed that, without very much practice, six men could undertake the loading procedure in twenty-four minutes. When the aircraft arrived at the delivery point the hull of the tank was simply released – the tracks were only about 14 in. off the ground – and dropped on to the runway. The driver climbed back in and ran it around to the side door for the turret to be fitted, the time for this operation being ten minutes.

British commentators were unable to see the logic in all this. A big aircraft like the DC4 needed a proper airfield in order to land at all, which would have to be well inside friendly territory or it would be a sitting target. In any case, the tank was not fit to fight until the turret was screwed on and the crew in place, so it could hardly be regarded as an operational procedure except in most unusual circumstances – say the delivery of a few tanks, in a hurry, to a distant island where they might be needed for internal security duties.

Development of the T9 was delayed when it was discovered that welding caused the face-hardened plates to crack, so it was redesigned with homogeneous armour. Standardised as the Light Tank M22, a few were supplied to Britain where it was known as the Locust. In order to improve its firepower the Littlejohn adaptor, designed for the 2-pounder, was modified to suit the 37-mm gun, but the tanks were used only once, during the Rhine Crossing, when they were delivered by Hamilcar gliders.

The American heavy tank programme was dominated, in the early part of the war, by what came to be known as the M6, a cast-hull tank weighing about 56 tons and mounting a 76.2-mm gun, along with its welded counterpart, the M6A1. By December 1942 the Americans had effectively lost interest in the project, although about 100, of both marks, were tentatively considered for Britain. Yet

it would appear that only two were ever actually ordered by the War Office, and this order was cancelled on 30 December 1943. A not dissimilar design, the heavy assault tank T14, will be discussed in context in the next chapter.

One thing most British visitors to the United States came away with at this time was an abiding and favourable impression of a virile and businesslike approach to the war. For those with any experience of British tank development, the contrast was very marked indeed. Even General Richardson, after a cool evaluation, was impressed. His tour through the system enabled him to draw together the threads in a way that was denied those whose duties kept them mainly in one place. For the benefit of his people in London he started by explaining the system. The Ordnance Board, who controlled research, design and development, kept in close touch with the users and tried to ensure that there was always something on offer that would appeal to them. This was then examined by the Armored Force Board, and if they liked what they saw it was submitted to the General Staff. Taking the larger view, this body then had the final word. At all stages in the process Richardson liked the way in which industry remained closely involved, determined to see that the Army got exactly what it wanted. He considered that something similar could, and should be organised in Britain, but he felt that while the Ministry of Supply continued to interpose itself between producer and user, no useful change could be expected. Thus, it seemed, gloomy predictions made in 1938 when the Ministry of Supply had been formed, were justified.

Early attempts to build a better medium tank, the T20, were frustrated at this stage because the General Staff felt that anything which interfered with developments in the M4 series would be more trouble than it was worth. Richardson reported on a chain of successors, including the petrol-electric T23 promoted by the General Electric Corporation, which finally bequeathed its turret to the 76-mm gun version of Sherman. Although they differed in detail, even down to the type of suspension, all these tanks had in common certain basic factors. One was a rear-mounted transmission and sprocket drive, which was not only more efficient but reduced overall height, and the silhouette was further improved by altering the basic hull shape. A feature that the Sherman had in common with the German Tiger was a hull form that spread out above the tracks, enclosing as much space under armour as possible. This had certain advantages, particularly in terms of turret ring diameter, but it increased bulk. It seems to have been a matter of policy in US tank design to place as much stowage as possible within the armoured hull, but from the T20 onwards this was reversed. Now the hull hung between the tracks and sheet steel track-guards were fitted, supporting a series of bins which carried many items of stowage externally. This step can probably be attributed to British influence from the Western Desert campaign.

78 One of the small batch of M26 Pershing tanks delivered to Britain at the end of the war.

79 The massive T18 Boarhound in Britain.

Medium tank development finally crystallised with the T26. Richardson reported on it in October 1943, although at that stage not even the wooden mock-up was available for inspection. Even so, he felt justified in advising the Director Royal Armoured Corps to order some. The Ordnance Department was very much in favour of it and the only bottle-neck seemed to be the Armoured Force Board, which was not convinced of the need for it. Ultimately it appeared as the heavy tank M26, or Pershing, with torsion bar suspension, 100-mm frontal armour and a 90-mm gun. It weighed around 41 tons and was driven by a 500-hp version of the Ford V8, which left it somewhat underpowered, but at least it was a tank to match the Tiger, if not necessarily the King Tiger. Britain placed an order for 500, but only a few were available for the US Army towards the end of the war in Europe, and of the handful delivered to Britain none saw active service.

One aspect of armoured warfare in which the United States was strongly influenced by Britain was armoured car design. This was primarily because the Americans had never really been well disposed to the armoured car as a weapon, and most of their designs were produced in response to British requirements. Foremost among these was the huge, eight-wheeled T18, or Boarhound, described as 'really a wheeled tank' in one British report. In fact it could trace its origins to the same concepts that had led to the South African and Canadian eight-wheelers

previously mentioned, both in this volume and in *The Great Tank Scandal* – something that could dominate the desert battlefield and slug it out with the big German cars which already had everyone spellbound. Designed by the Yellow Truck and Coach Company, the Boarhound was powered by a pair of GMC six-cylinder engines driving all eight wheels. In its final form it mounted a 57-mm gun, but it was not ready for production until 1943 and by then the requirement for it had vanished. An order for 2,500 was drastically cut back to around thirty machines, none of which entered service.

The Chevrolet division of General Motors produced quite a selection of good-looking six-wheeled armoured cars, again presumably with British custom in mind, but none ever reached production status. Of these their T19 is said to have influenced the design of the post-war British Alvis Saladin, while the best of them, standardised as the M38, might have been adopted by the US Army if the end of the war had not intervened. Chevrolet had more success with their four-wheeled T17, which was produced specifically to British requirements and entered service as the Staghound. It was a big car, armed with nothing better than a 37-mm gun, but it proved easy to drive, especially compared with something like the British AEC. In July 1943 each British armoured car regiment in the United Kingdom received fourteen Staghounds for evaluation, and in due course they served in Italy and North West Europe with British, Commonwealth and Allied armies, including the Belgians. Variations included the T17E2, mounting a pair of Browning machine-guns in an anti-aircraft turret designed by Frazer Nash, and T17E3, a close support version with a 75-mm howitzer in an open-topped turret, which never got beyond the prototype stage. British and New Zealand troops in Italy developed their own close support version, known as the Staghound II, which employed the old 3-in. howitzer used in certain British tanks. Then there was the Staghound III. This was developed in Britain as part of the policy of providing reconnaissance units with greater firepower and began, in the case of the Staghound, with an attempt to squeeze the British 75-mm gun into the regular Staghound turret. This proved quite impossible and, after casting around for alternatives, it was decided to adapt the 6-pounder turret of the Crusader Mark III. Plans were first announced in November 1943 with the intention of building 100, to be issued on the basis of one per troop to all armoured car regiments. The proposal was rejected outright by units fighting in Italy, who were perfectly happy with their 75-mm half-tracks on account of their ability to move off the road. DRAC reported in May 1944 that firing trials were already completed, but added that, due to the urgency with which it was required, only modifications essential to improved fightability were acceptable. Clearly, since the Crusader turret had already been adapted to take the 6-pounder, there was no problem fitting the 75-mm gun in its place, proving that the Crusader itself could

80 *The overpowering effect of a 75-mm Crusader turret fitted to the Staghound hull. The hull machine-gun, not normally fitted to a Staghound III, suggests that this might be the prototype conversion.*

have been upgunned to 75-mm had the need arisen. The only other obvious change was to the layout of the roof hatches, which were staggered to comply with revised crew stations. The Polish Army in Britain is understood to have been given some, but in November 1944 it was announced that both the Staghound III and AEC III, the only other 75-mm gun armoured car, were to be 'eliminated' since there was no longer a requirement for them. Whatever elimination entailed, it evidently did not mean wholesale scrapping, since some Staghound IIIs turned up in Danish and Canadian service after the war.

When the Americans did come to design an armoured car for their own use, it proved to be a good deal smaller than anything so far created for the British. In fact it could be described as a cross between a scout car and a small tank destroyer, since it mounted a 37-mm gun in an open-top turret, yet retained a low silhouette, six-wheel drive mobility off the road and a good top speed of 55 mph. It paid for this to some extent with thin armour, and was notoriously vulnerable to mines, but it proved popular with the US Army. The Ford Motor Company built over 12,000 of them under the designation M8. To the British it was known as the Greyhound; its limited service in Italy has already been described.

Despite the fact that no vehicle like the Universal Carrier was ever adopted by nations other than Britain and the Commonwealth, the type remained immensely popular with those armies and to meet the continuing demand

the United States was drawn into the production programme. A Ford Motor Company design was accepted and the British Tank Mission placed orders for 30,000 under the American designation T16. It was a lengthened version of the British model with an extra road wheel added to the suspension, and it relied on lever steering instead of the track warping system devised by Vickers-Armstrong. A Fighting Vehicle Proving Establishment report on six pre-production models revealed problems with oil-cooling, failure of the tapered roller bearings in the suspension at 2,200 miles, and a loss of efficiency in the steering brakes due to the ingress of mud. These were all corrected in the next six vehicles, and it was subse-

81 *A fully equipped T16 Carrier photographed in the United States.*

quently stated that 3,500 production machines had left the factory and were awaiting shipment. Production again seems to have been slow in getting under way and the modest number that were delivered saw most service in post-war years. The Americans showed no interest in the type themselves, although it was said that they were considering a lighter, narrower version for use in jungle warfare. A Mark II version, the T16E2, was planned for 1945, by which time one might have thought something a bit more modern could have been designed, but the only obvious change was a modification to the suspension. Among other things this would feature disc roadwheels with synthetic rubber tyres. This model, however, was cancelled before production began.

If the Americans had any vehicle which could be compared with the Universal Carrier, at least in terms of purpose if not design, it was the M3 half-track. The type had evolved from the White Scout Car, using a rear bogie with rubber and fabric tracks developed from the pre-war French Kegresse system. It had one great advantage over contemporary German half-tracks, in having a driven front axle. Mass production in the United States commenced in 1941 with versions by White, naturally enough, as well as Autocar and Diamond T. They were seen primarily as armoured personnel carriers capable of maintaining station with tanks under most battlefield conditions as well as keeping up with wheeled vehicles on the road. Actual armour protection was limited to a modest 8 mm and there was no overhead protection for the passengers but, as with most American designs, they were extremely rugged, workmanlike vehicles, destined for an extraordinarily long career.

Quite when British interest was first stimulated is not clear. We have already noticed the adoption of a self-propelled gun version first encountered in Tunisia, but it seems reasonable to assume that British Army representatives in Washington were already aware of it. Since the half-track does not appear in the British Tank Mission archives it must have been dealt with by another agency, and this supposition is enhanced by the fact that, in British service, the type was always classified as a 15-cwt truck. Demand for the Standard Types, manufactured by those firms already listed, soon began to stretch the supply so, in order to meet Lend-Lease requirements from Britain and the Soviet Union, a Substitute Standard Design was introduced in 1942 by the International Harvester Corporation. Most of the half-tracks supplied to Britain came from this source. These included the M5 and M9 (thirteen- and ten-seater personnel carriers respectively) and the M14, which mounted multiple heavy machine-guns on an anti-aircraft turntable at the back.

Just like the Universal Carrier, the US half-track was rarely used for its intended purposes in British service. In Italy, it seems, the basic APC function never materialised to any great extent and by the time British forces were active again in North West Europe the majority of them

had been relegated to other tasks. The M14s all lost their gun and were converted into APCs, load carriers or command vehicles, while others became armoured ambulances. Writing after the war in Europe had ended, a medical officer compared casualty collection from tanks between the desert, where he had been equipped with a Dingo Scout car and some wheeled 15-cwt trucks, and Europe where he had half-tracks. The advent of the latter made a great difference, not only to the medical officer, but also to his patients. In the desert, since one could not take ordinary trucks into the middle of a tank battle, he would tour about in his Dingo, identifying casualties whom he would evacuate in the scout car, always trusting that there were not too many at any one time. His half-tracks, by contrast, were not only armoured but capable of carrying four stretcher patients. In Europe they were issued on a scale of four per tank regiment and the normal practice was for one to accompany each squadron into action. They were equipped with panels of wood and corrugated iron to erect temporary shelters as first aid posts and the officer advised that the half-track should approach the rear of a knocked out tank and turn around before attempting to load the injured.

As a supply carrier the half-track was often loaded well above the official 15-cwt capacity, while the command version contained extra radio sets and a table for the commander to work at. A raised canvas roof, with clear panels let into it, was erected over the top of the body. Official user comments on the half-tracks are not easy to find and the British Army made no attempt to copy, or improve on the design. Rather they set Vauxhall Motors the task of copying the big German half-tracks, although this project failed while the American types soldiered on for many years after the war.

The Americans have been regularly castigated by British commentators for their apparent failure to adopt British types of specialised armour prior to D-Day. This is not the place to discuss such a subject, beyond pointing out that British industry had quite enough to do at the time without trying to supply the United States Army as well. In any case the statement is not true. Both CDL and DD tanks were built in the USA for use by both allies, and America was developing her own family of special-purpose AFVs, every bit as varied and ingenious as their British counterparts, if not always as successful.

As recounted in *The Great Tank Scandal*, Michael Dewar visited Clearwater, Florida at Christmas 1940 to examine Donald Roebling's Alligator amphibian, a number of which were subsequently obtained for training by British units. By 1942 a Landing Vehicle Tracked Mark 2 had appeared, which used Stuart tank automotive components with a similar rear-engine, front-drive layout, but its tactical role was changing. From an amphibious load carrier for ship-to-shore resupply, it was now evolving into an amphibious personnel carrier, at least in the Pacific, and this brought a demand for some degree of armour

82 *Typically encumbered, an International M9A1 half-track in British service.*

83 *A well-laden LVT 2 takes to the water.*

protection. Further it was not seen as ideally suited to this purpose. Its great bulk, upon leaving the water, made it a choice target, while the infantry passengers were dangerously exposed as they clambered over the sides and dropped to the ground in action. Thus in 1943 the Food Machinery Corporation undertook a redesign which appeared as the LVT (4), in which the automotive package was concentrated at the front, enabling a hinged ramp to be fitted at the rear. This not only enabled troops to disembark in relative safety, it also expanded the functions of the vehicle to the extent that it could now load and carry small vehicles and towed weapons. Both types were supplied to Britain, where their role will be discussed in a later chapter.

American involvement in the DD tank programme came about as a direct result of General Eisenhower's decision to adopt the type for use by the United States Army on D-Day. Initial production centred on the radial-engined M4 and M4A1 tanks, built to current British standards, which were issued to American, British and Canadian units. But the ultimate model, the DD Mark III was an all-American version. As a result of tragic American losses off Omaha Beach on D-Day, much greater attention was paid to structural rigidity of the flotation screen. This included three-in. diameter top-rails, high-pressure pneumatic columns and relocation of the steel support struts, all of which were made self-locking. By this stage Sherman tank development had advanced to incorporate the 76-mm gun and new horizontal volute suspension with 23-in. wide tracks; two samples converted to the DD role were supplied to Britain in 1945, where the designation Sherman IIIAY DDIII was adopted. This indicated that the tanks were all of the diesel Sherman III (M4A2) type, while A signified the 76-mm gun and Y the new suspension. An order for 300 of this type, later reduced to 200, was placed for delivery to South East Asia Command, but never fulfilled when Japan capitulated.

As explained in Chapter 3 the Americans supplied CDL turrets in response to British requirements, but they also raised a number of special tank battalions of their own to operate them. These used the original M3 and cast-hull M3A1 versions of the Lee and, after training in the USA, came over to Britain where they worked-up alongside their British counterparts in South Wales. However, despite

84 One of the few Sherman IIIAY DDIII tanks supplied to Britain, seen here with the framework erected but no screen or air-tubes fitted. Notice the 76-mm gun, T23 turret and horizontal volute suspension.

85 A Canadian Medium Tank Grizzly.

moving across to France in August 1944 they were never used operationally and subsequently reverted to conventional Sherman battalions.

In his diary, whenever he felt the need to emphasise his team's role in persuading the Americans to build the Sherman, Michael Dewar would explain that the Canadian-built Ram was his example. Undoubtedly he was overstating the case, but what he could not have foreseen was that the Canadians would finish up by assembling Shermans when Ram production came to an end. Plans were announced in 1942, but it was mid-1943 before the last Ram II came off the Montreal Locomotive Works production line and the Grizzly, Canada's name for their Sherman, replaced it. Based on the cast-hull M4A1 it was really an assembly job because the components were mainly brought in from across the border. Certain detail changes were made to suit British requirements, but production ceased at the end of the year when less than 200 had been completed, and most of these were retained for training in Canada.

Canada was also a major contributor to the Universal Carrier programme and in 1943 was asked to develop something that would replace the British Loyd. Built by Ford of Canada, and known initially as the Campbell Carrier, it looked similar to the American T16, although it retained the Vickers method of steering. Early production models were beset with mechanical problems and by the time these were cured it was too late to see much active service. Known ultimately as the Windsor it was designed for roles such as mortar carrying and anti-tank gun towing. It seems, to some extent, to have been Canada's fate during the war to build what amounted to copies of

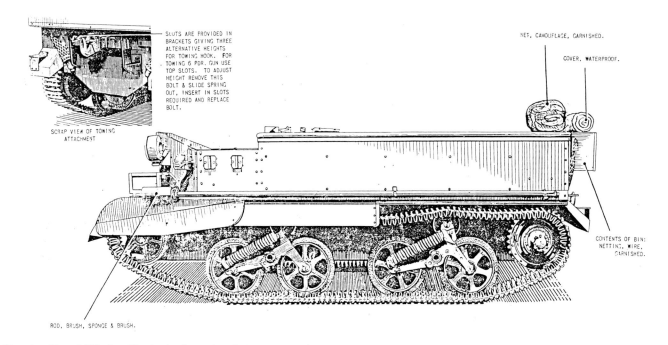

SLOTS ARE PROVIDED IN BRACKETS GIVING THREE ALTERNATIVE HEIGHTS FOR TOWING HOOK. FOR TOWING 6 PDR. GUN USE TOP SLOTS. TO ADJUST HEIGHT REMOVE THIS BOLT & SLIDE SPRING OUT, INSERT IN SLOTS REQUIRED AND REPLACE BOLT.

SCRAP VIEW OF TOWING ATTACHMENT

NET, CAMOUFLAGE, GARNISHED.

COVER, WATERPROOF.

CONTENTS OF BIN: NETTING, WIRE, GARNISHED.

ROD, BRUSH, SPONGE & BRUSH.

Drawing G: *A Windsor Carrier in the anti-tank gun tractor role.*

86   A Ford Lynx scout car – Canada's answer to the Dingo – on test at Chertsey.

87   A well-laden C15 armoured truck. It even carries a PIAT on the offside wing.

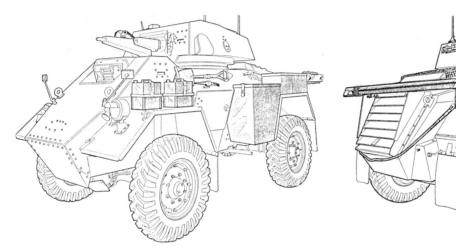

Drawing H: Sketches of the Fox armoured car showing stowage arrangements.

British vehicles, which cannot have done much to stimulate initiative. Ingenuity, and good engineering practice were called for, but mainly in adapting British concepts to Canadian production techniques, and this can plainly be seen in the Lynx. This was a two-man scout car, outwardly very similar to the Daimler Dingo, yet lacking that vehicle's sophisticated drive system. Built by Ford of Canada it consisted of a Dingo-style hull resting on a rear-engined, four-wheel drive chassis. It was a good deal more powerful than the British scout car, having a Ford V8 engine installed, but it lacked the advantages of the Daimler's independent suspension and Wilson transmission. The Fox, likewise, was a Canadian counterpart to the British Humber armoured car. Built by General Motors Canada it mounted a three-man turret like the Humber Mark III but employed Browning, rather than Besa, machine-guns. The first Lynx was at MEE in Britain by May 1943, where it earned favourable reports, but by October it was announced that production was delayed while various modifications were put in hand. Neither type enjoyed any great prominence, although a Mark II version of the Lynx was produced with a more robust suspension.

88   The Canadian-based CAPLAD multi-purpose armoured vehicle.

There is no doubt that one of the most unexpected success stories of the war, as far as Allied armoured vehicles were concerned, was the White Scout Car. Being a pre-war design it is hardly surprising that it did not find this success as a scout car, but in other roles more suited to that of an armoured lorry. Clearly there was a need for such a thing, and Canada was selected to design the replacement. The result was the General Motors armoured truck C15TA. It had a good deal of the Otter Light Reconnaissance car about it, but employed a more powerful GM six-cylinder engine and two-ratio gearbox. A fully enclosed version appeared in small numbers as an armoured ambulance but the majority were open-topped and equipped as trucks or eight-seater personnel carriers. Extremely popular wherever it served, the C15 lasted for years after the war, but it never succeeded in ousting the venerable White, which at one stage looked like going on for ever. A logical development of the armoured truck, or maybe a wheeled version of the Universal Carrier was CAPLAD, an acronym for Car, Armoured Personnel, Light Aid Detachment, Ambulance, Demolition. This was a genuine Anglo-Canadian project, the true Canadian prototype being based on General Motors Fox components. However, since the British version used Canadian Ford mechanics the two can reasonably be classed together. Outwardly they looked remarkably like the earlier Indian wheeled carriers, but the war ended before they reached production status, and the project was dropped.

It remains to record two vehicles that were indigenous Canadian designs. One was a tiny, air-portable vehicle known as the Tracked Jeep. Designed in Canada it was built by Marmon-Herrington and Willys in the United States using the latter firm's Jeep engine. Two marks were built, but only a handful of each were completed before the project was dropped. Naturally enough, Canada had considerable experience of building and operating over-snow vehicles, some of which were of considerable interest to the military. Marketed as the Snowmobile one developed into an armoured carrier, powered by a Cadillac

V8 engine, and seems to have proved suitable for all ground and weather conditions, since a sample vehicle was tested over mud and swamps by MEE in Italy and shortly after the war another was used experimentally on the otherwise impassable sand sea of the Qattara Depression in, of all places, the Sahara Desert!

Canadian involvement in the development of specialised armour was crucial. Indeed, although they could not be said to have invented it, there is no doubt that it was Canadian engineers who reinvigorated the project at a critical stage and certainly broadened its application, notably in developing the Churchill AVRE. However, much of the work they did was so closely intertwined with the larger British programme that it cannot be studied in isolation. Here we will only attempt to examine some projects which were distinctly Canadian in origin and development.

90   An armoured Snowmobile on test in Britain.

89   The Mark II version of the little Marmon-Herrington Tracked Jeep.

91 *A Sherman fitted with the Canadian Indestructible Roller Device. Both rollers are shown in the normal trailing position.*

Most prominent among these was the optimistically named Canadian Indestructible Roller Device (CIRD). The British anti-mine rollers all suffered from the basic flaw that they were eminently destructible. A tank propelling the AMCRA device would enter a mined area with four substantial rollers intact, two ahead of each track. It was a lottery as to which would go first. In the ideal scenario three, or even possibly four mines would be detonated, destroying a roller each, before the tank came to any harm, but in the worst case it only needed two in succession on one side of the tank, followed by a third which was detonated by the tank. Result: disaster. As already explained, it was not the purpose of this equipment to try and force a path across a minefield – all that was required of it was to roll the ground in a suspect area until one went off, and then up would come flails to do the rest. Even so, it was a wasteful way of doing the work and General Worthington, commanding 4th Canadian Division in Britain, thought he had a better notion.

His idea was to mount the roller on the end of a swinging arm so that it would be thrown clear by the blast and then fall back ready to be used again. The project was handed over to the Obstacle Assault Centre, which produced a prototype on a Churchill. It passed through a number of development stages, which need not all be chronicled; a general description will suffice. The key to success was substantial construction and high-quality materials. A massive pair of arms, pivoting about a bearing roughly halfway down the tank, stretched out ahead of each track. At the forward extremity the arms were joined by a nickel steel cross-shaft, that rested in resilient mountings and from which a pair of shorter arms depended, free to swing around this crossbar, and kept in line by the side pressure of large helical springs threaded on to it. At the business end of each of these arms was the roller. It was of anything between 18 in. and 2 ft in diameter, about 15 in. wide and made from solid armour, so that the average roller weighed 1 ton.

In action the vehicle advanced with both rollers trailing from the crossbar until one of them ran over a mine. The detonation lifted both roller and arm, throwing them forward in an arc until they struck the ground ahead of the crossbar where a short spade, on the end of the arm, stuck into the ground. Now, as the tank advanced, the spade dug in, the main projecting arm on that side of the tank rose upwards, distorting the frame, and then settled down again once the roller had passed underneath and resumed its proper station. As with all these devices once one fault was corrected another showed up; two examples will suffice. Early trials against British Mark IV mines resulted in the roller spreading within its cradle and failing to revolve, making it almost impossible for the tank to push it along. This was corrected by slimming down the roller, but later problems arose with the stub axles, which broke up after a few detonations. Investigations by the English Steel Corporation resulted in an axle which survived forty-eight successive detonations of double Mark IV mines, although the number of rollers destroyed during the trial is not recorded; the usual average was about one every ten Teller-mines. CIRD was developed for the Churchill and Sherman, although the latter tank could not cope with the heavier rollers, and in April 1945 a version was produced which fitted Cromwell. Sherman CIRDs were issued as pilot tanks, on the scale of one per troop, to flail regiments in North West Europe but withdrawn before the end of 1944.

In an attempt to beat the mine roller tank at its own game the Germans came up with the tilt igniter mine. This was an ordinary Teller-mine buried upside down with a 2-ft long rod from the igniter poking up through the ground. Sown among conventional mines, one only had to be nudged by the hull front of a tank to be detonated beneath its belly. In order to counter this, a light frame was added, between the rollers on a CIRD attachment, to knock over the rod and set the mine off ahead of the tank.

Again, as already recorded, it was the Canadians that saved the Carrier flamethrower project by adopting Ronson when it had been rejected by Britain. However, the later British development, the Wasp, was such an improvement that it was ultimately adopted by both armies. One of the original requirements was that the fuel reservoirs be located within the hull of the vehicles which, in a Universal Carrier, placed a considerable premium on space. Recalling Ronson, the Canadians could see no reason for this. If the fuel tank was placed outside the hull at the back it was probably more vulnerable, but at least it was further away from the crew if it did go off. They therefore initiated development of their own version, the Wasp II(C) which also used panels of plastic armour to improve protection in the crew area.

The Canadians also installed Wasp flamethrowers in some Ram Kangaroos. They selected late production versions without the subsidiary turret and fitted a flame projector in place of the hull machine-gun. The turret ring was then plated over and a small cupola installed. Known as the Badger, a few were operating with Canadian armoured units during the last months of the war.

6 Consolidation

The Cromwell and Centaur tanks which had been sent over to the United States, and which were the subjects of General Richardson's bitter remarks recorded in the last chapter, were tested in comparison with an M4A3 Sherman in the summer of 1943. A summary of the results included a league table of man-hours required to repair or replace failed items; figures that did not take into account time spent waiting for the parts to arrive. The Centaur required 202 man-hours and the Cromwell 199; the Ford-engined Sherman required only thirty-nine. By way of mitigation it was explained that the Centaur, T1840054, and Cromwell, T121154 were from the first batch of ten built in each case. 'They have every known fault in them and are thoroughly unsatisfactory machines', according to the Ministry of Supply, which raises the question of why they should have been sent to America at all.

In the light of these results, it was decided to repeat the trial on a grander scale in Britain under the code name Exercise Dracula, which was presumably intended to go straight to the jugular. Fourteen tanks were involved, including Centaurs, Cromwells and Shermans of the M4A2 (twin diesel) and M4A4 (multibank petrol) varieties. The trials involved long road and cross-country runs in the Bovington area, longer journeys visiting other armoured formations, and a firing test at Lulworth Camp. In their reports every single commentator came down heavily in favour of the Shermans, with the palm going to the diesel model. Runs were made in daylight only, at least in theory, and although both British cruisers had a considerable edge on speed they always limped in last.

Taking a typical day, the first home every time was the M4A2, followed closely by the M4A4 which, due to its greater fuel consumption, had to refuel once on the road. After a quick last parade their crews were released for a hot meal right on time. Then the receiving troops settled down to wait. They included guides stationed along the route, refuelling crews, fitters and the controlling officers. Invariably the Cromwells arrived next, usually well after dark, and then the Centaurs straggled in, often during the small hours. Last parade could take up to one and a half hours, so that crews went to a late, and very unappetising cold supper. Morning starts were scheduled for 8.30, by which time the Sherman crews sauntered down to their tanks, jumped in and drove off, while incidental problems meant that the Cromwells and Centaurs got away late. Major breakdowns appear to have been the exception; rather it was the need for continual maintenance *en route* which held up the British tanks. Clutches gave out, brakes

often needed adjusting and, in the Centaurs, so much oil leaked from the engine that the radiators had to be cleaned down at regular intervals. Track life was good but track adjustment difficult and hydraulic controls were in need of constant attention and maintenance. It sounded like a catalogue of disasters. Reporting on the exercise, Major K M Ronald of the Westminster Dragoons confessed that after two and a half years' experience with British tanks, he was forced to change all his ideas. From believing the Sherman to be overrated he now felt that it was superior to anything Britain had produced up to date, adding: 'The commander of a unit equipped with Shermans can be confident of taking 99 per cent of his vehicles into battle [while] if he were equipped with Cromwells or Centaurs he would be in a continuous state of anxiety as to whether enough of his tanks would reach the battlefield to carry out the normal tasks expected of his unit.'

Major Clifford, OC of the Dracula Squadron stated that he would prefer not to take a squadron of Centaurs on active service, since they were underpowered, unreliable and in need of more maintenance in relation to running time than was justified. The Cromwell, he felt, had the makings of a wonderful fighting machine, although he reckoned that it was not yet out of the experimental stage. Despite a top speed of 40 mph, which it was agreed the crews enjoyed, he regarded it as unwise to exceed 30 mph except in an emergency since, if one did so, a host of track and suspension troubles could be expected. On the Sherman he started to eulogise: 'almost beyond reproach . . . utterly reliable . . . infinitely superior', and so on. Just to rub it in, the Shermans did best on the gunnery trials too. Only one of the British cruisers could fire without the attentions of a gun fitter, while the Shermans simply adjusted their sights, drove up to the firing point and fired all their guns without a hitch.

Although it was not mentioned in the first trial report, there was one other aspect of Exercise Dracula that did do some good for all British tank crews. The event was used as a comparative trial of various crew garments that included a denim one-piece overall and a waterproof oversuit, both of which were regarded as an unqualified success.

If Dracula achieved nothing else, it seems to have sounded the virtual death-knell of Centaur as a front-line tank. At the Prime Minister's instigation production was cut back from an authorised total of 2,700 machines to 2,000, many of which would be allocated to subsidiary roles, notably as anti-aircraft tanks. Nothing was made public at the time but, in the subtle way governments have of letting cats out of bags, the tank was taken off the Secret List and details released to the press in April 1944. 'NEW TANK – OFF THE SECRET LIST' said a headline in the *Sunday Chronicle* over a photograph of the tank. The caption described it as 'Britain's latest monster tank . . . mounting a six-pounder gun, it has a three-man turret . . . this powerful new British weapon . . . may play an important role in the second front'. An innocuous enough step in itself, it set alarm bells ringing at Westminster in the ears of certain MPs who already had more than enough doubts about the quality of British tanks. Why, they demanded to know, was this being done now? What was the government's purpose in releasing details of a tank which had not yet seen active service? Could there be something wrong with it? Major S S Hammersley, an officer with Tank Corps experience in the Great War and now MP for East Willesden, together with that veteran campaigner Richard Stokes, gave the Prime Minister and Sir Andrew Duncan a very hard time. Acrimonious exchanges ended with Stokes asking the Prime Minister to order a Churchill and Tiger to be brought into New Palace Yard so that Members might compare them. This was refused, causing a Mr McGovern to chip in: 'Will the Prime Minister be prepared to take charge of a Churchill tank and allow the Hon. Member for Ipswich [Mr Stokes] to take charge of a Tiger tank? To which the Prime Minister growled, 'I think it might be one way of settling the difference.'

Churchill and Sir Andrew (the Minister of Supply) were supported in this petty debate by the Secretary of State for War, Sir James Grigg – the formidable P J Grigg described by Jack Smithers as the rudest man in the Civil Service.* Yet Sir Andrew and Grigg had clashed fiercely during the previous summer, and the Centaur had been at the bottom of that. A series of *SECRET & PERSONAL* letters which passed between them have survived in official files, and they reveal a very unhappy situation at the top. Grigg talked of 'intriguing and schoolgirl quarrels' between Commander Micklem of the Tank Board and the weapons guru General Sir Campbell Clarke. He had also wanted to know if the War Office was kept fully and punctually informed. Reports from troops suggested that Centaur was proving unreliable but the implication was that the Minister had kept quiet about it. Worse still was the matter of the new High Velocity 75-mm gun. Until mid-July 1943, Grigg claimed, he had been led to believe that it would go into Cromwell in due course, but he now understood that this could not be, because the turret ring was too small. He denied any imputation of sparring for position, but had finished: 'I cannot go on any longer living in a fool's paradise.' Sir Andrew had attempted to restore the situation by appointing his Parliamentary

Secretary, Duncan Sandys as a direct liaison with General Sir Ronald Weeks at the War Office. Further he had cracked a whip over Clarke and Micklem, but in respect of the HV 75-mm gun he had been able to prove that it had not been until the end of June that anyone had realised it would not fit Cromwell. Duncan's comments on the Centaur had been more defensive, explaining that it had been suffering from 'the usual troubles . . . invariably experienced with a new tank' but then going on to admit that the Liberty engine was far from ideal and not comparable with the Meteor. He also made a point not noted elsewhere, that the Liberty, being that much longer than the Meteor, made greater demands on available space inside the hull and that for this reason it had not been an easy matter to improve the performance of the clutch. However, the Minister had not been keen to make any further reductions in Centaur production. Such a step, he had claimed, would inevitably have led to such a sacrifice of production capacity that it would have been impossible to get it established again in 1945 when Meteor production was expected to expand.

These exchanges seem to reveal that after four years of war, things had still not changed to any worthwhile degree. Here, in one letter, we have the admission that Cromwell, as designed, could not be upgunned, yet the Minister responsible for production was not going to make any great changes, he clearly intended Centaur/Cromwell construction to achieve a peak in 1945, despite the fact that two new and more powerful models were under consideration.

These new models, the short-term A34 Comet and long-term A41 Centurion, will be considered later. For the present it is necessary to examine two schemes to upgun existing tanks. Research had shown that the ideal anti-tank weapon was a piece of 3-in. calibre firing a 17-pound shot, and plans to develop such a gun had been authorised in November 1940. A year later the first pilot weapons were undergoing trials and a meeting of the Tank Board held on 9 December 1941 considered whether such a gun could be fitted into a tank. As for what happened next, it is really a matter of who one is prepared to believe. The official line is that a 17-pounder gun tank was ordered, presumably around the New Year of 1942, from the Birmingham Railway Carriage & Wagon Company. They were the obvious choice, since the new tank was to be based on A27M Cromwell components, and they were the production parents for that tank. Design of the gun-mounting and turret was placed in the hands of Stothert & Pitt of Bath. BRC&W's task, therefore, was to modify a Cromwell hull so that it could accept a 70-in. turret ring and the extra weight associated with a bigger turret. This they did firstly by widening the hull around the fighting compartment and then by lengthening it to accept an extra wheel station on each side, which enlarged the hull and spread the weight over a larger area. Stothert & Pitt's part in the proceedings is not quite so well recorded. Certainly

---

* A J Smithers, *A New Excalibur*, Leo Cooper, 1986.

92 *An early A30 Challenger posed alongside the captured Tiger at Chertsey. Both tanks have their respective armour thickness, in inches,* *chalked on them. It does not make an inspiring comparison.*

they designed and built the new turret, but it is not entirely clear if they had already begun to do this for the superheavy tank TOG II and then adapted it to suit the cruiser hull, or whether the turret was designed for the improved Cromwell and then also fitted to TOG II because it was there. On balance the second scenario appears to be the more likely.

For an alternative view one has to turn to W A Robotham of Rolls-Royce. One chapter of his autobiography, referred to earlier, is a thinly-veiled claim to have originated the new tank with his team at Belper. Due credit is given to Stothert & Pitt for the turret, but BRC&W are portrayed only as skilled artisans, fitting together what Robotham and his men designed. There may well be a good deal of truth in this – the surviving records are not too clear – but Robotham damages his case with some wilder claims which invite doubts. To begin with, he dates the inception of Challenger, as the new tank was called, to 1943, following the debut of Germany's Tiger and goes on to claim that, in order to have it ready for D-Day, existing components had to be used. Now there are documents enough to show that when the A30 Challenger project was first conceived the Tiger was quite unknown to the Allies or was, at best, only a vague and exaggerated rumour,[*] while D-Day was little more than a pipe-dream. Robotham must have regarded Challenger as

his baby. Why else should he have gone to such lengths to defend it against post-war critics, while pleading ignorance of user opinion and its wartime record, such as it was?

Rugged though it may be, there are some things you should never do to a tank unless you want it to fail. One is to increase the weight beyond what the suspension can bear, the other is to mess about with the L over C ratio, where L is the length of track in contact with the ground and C the distance across the tank from one track centre to the other. It is important that the relationship between these two figures be as close as possible. If the tank, and consequently its track, gets longer without the tracks being spaced further apart, then the vehicle is more difficult to steer. Challenger was about 6 ft longer than Cromwell, but no wider, so steering was bound to be harder, and the resulting strain on the suspension that much greater. When the idea of a 17-pounder armed tank was first mooted it was laid down, as a matter of policy, that it should have the same standard of protection as the tank it was to support; in the case of Challenger this would be Cromwell. As the design work began, some military authorities suggested that a Cromwell should be over-weighted in order to test the suspension, but this idea was rejected out of hand by the Ministry of Supply, who assured them that it would be quite all right. Events proved the Ministry wrong but it being impossible to reduce the armour thickness of the hull, the turret was severely attacked. The frontal turret armour was reduced to 63-mm, from 75-mm on a Cromwell, while the latter's

---

[*] D J Fletcher (ed), *Tiger!*, HMSO, 1986.

side armour thickness of 65-mm was cut down to a mere 40-mm on Challenger, yet the Stothert & Pitt turret was a target like a barn door compared with the little box fitted to the Cromwell. In fact the overall height of Challenger was by no means as great as it seems, but this is due to the relative sizes of turret and hull.

It must be remembered that when Challenger was first being considered most British tanks were armed with a 2-pounder gun, the anti-tank round for which would almost fit into the pocket. By comparison, the 17-pounder round was a substantial lump of metal and it was felt that one loader would not only tire quickly, he would also have difficulty collecting ammunition from all around the turret. Thus it was decided to provide an extra loader, bringing the turret crew up to four: commander, gunner, loader/wireless operator and extra loader. To balance this, the hull machine-gunner was eliminated and his area taken up with increased ammunition stowage, inside an armoured bin for the first time in a British tank. As a consequence the Challenger turret was huge by contemporary standards, and it had a couple of other features worth commenting upon. One was the new Metadyne power traverse system, the other a device for raising the turret a few millimetres to prevent it from getting jammed. Since the turret ring was not protected, as originally designed, there was always a risk that even a glancing blow at this point would jam it solid. to overcome this a device was incorporated in the base of the turret, which rested on a massive phosphor bronze ball, that would enable a crew member to crank the turret up sufficiently to clear such an obstruction.

Three pilot models of A30 were building at Birmingham in May 1942 and the first complete one was inspected by the Tank Board at Farnborough on 13 August 1942. Robotham tells a story of this event as a means of pointing up the curious military attitude to security. Bearing in mind that Challenger was, at this time, classified Top Secret, he claims that the tank despatched to Farnborough (from Belper by his account, not Birmingham) was carefully sheeted down on its transporter to hide every detail from prying eyes. After the demonstration in Long Valley Robotham was driving through Farnborough on his way home when he came upon 'his' tank, parked outside a pub, with the crew perched on top of the turret clutching pints in their hands, and not a vestige of tarpaulin to be seen anywhere.

Pilot B was inspected by the Tank Board at Lulworth on 21 January 1943, where it had been sent for user trials. Apparently this was delivered from Stothert & Pitt at Bath, where Pilot C was then nearing completion. Trials revealed that the heavy turret was very difficult to traverse when the tank was parked sideways on a slope, and that the crew positions were uncomfortable and difficult to work in. However, the most damning report was issued by the Chief Inspector, Gunnery at the Armoured Fighting Vehicle School, Lulworth. He questioned the entire con-

cept. Again we must remember that when this report was published, on 23 January 1943, British troops were still fighting in North Africa with a wealth of desert warfare experience behind them, yet at this date they had not confronted the Tiger. To begin with, the report pointed out, present British doctrine laid down that it was not a tank's normal role to fight other tanks. Yet the 17-pounder, being an anti-tank gun and a very good one, the writer assumed that A30 was built to fight tanks. As a consequence his main concern was with the armour thickness. Taking the latest model of Panzer IV Special as its most dangerous opponent, at the maximum effective range for both tanks of 3,000 yards (and assuming a head-on confrontation) the Challenger could penetrate the Panzer IV, while the German's shot would bounce off A30. However, at closer ranges the British tank was at a severe disadvantage, even compared with Cromwell, due to its vulnerability, slow rate of fire and limited ammunition stowage. Since he perceived that desert warfare was coming to an end, and likely to do so before A30 ever entered service, he questioned its value. Accepting that the 17-pounder was an excellent anti-tank gun he claimed that A30 was, by definition, not a tank, nor was it suitable as a self-propelled anti-tank weapon on account of its size. It was, he said, a White Elephant. His penultimate paragraph is worth quoting from for, brief as it is, it sums up that essence of good tank design which Britain had consistently ignored.

'When a tactical requirement is laid down for a tank for a special role, the gun is the first thing to decide on, and then the turret armour required, and not till then is it possible to consider what hull and suspension is necessary to carry it.' His final recommendation began: 'That the A30 should not be proceeded with . . .'; it went unheeded. On 10 February 1943, 200 were ordered. On 23 November 1943, following further developments, it was stated that 'A30 satifies the General Staff requirement for a cruiser tank with high armour piercing performance but no more than 200 will be built although these would be first priority at the expense of Cromwell production.'

From the initial design stage to final production, Challenger occupied well over two years, an average period in time of war, except for the fact that the tank was hardly a novel design, so much as a dramatically modified Cromwell. Seen in that light, it appears to be an unreasonably long period in which to produce a tank which was not anywhere near as good as it might have been; just the usual mixed bag of compromises that the Tank Board and Ministry normally cobbled together between themselves. The officer from Lulworth who had criticised Challenger was probably Lieutenant-Colonel George Witheridge RTR. At the outbreak of war he had been part of the experimental team at Lulworth but he had been transferred to the Western Desert, only to be seriously injured after being blown out of his tank at Gazala. Later he was seconded to Fort Knox in the United States, where he formed a very favourable impression of the Sherman and considered how to upgun it. Returning to his new post at Lulworth in June 1943 Witheridge was dismayed to see Challenger, and immediately considered how the 17-pounder might be fitted into Sherman instead, even if this meant designing a new turret. He soon discovered that somebody had beaten him to it.

Major George Brighty, another original member of the Lulworth team, had managed to get a 17-pounder into a conventional Sherman turret, but only by employing the most unconventional means, with the gun mounted rigidly into the mantlet and no facility whatever for recoil. This was a drastic step and Witheridge was not at all sure that he approved of it. However, he staged a trial, firing three rounds from outside the turret by means of a lanyard and, when nothing dreadful happened, getting inside to bang away a further seven. He concluded that it was a workable proposition, once certain small faults had been ironed out, but he did not envy the turret crew in such a tank and advised Brighty to try again. At this point Witheridge was firmly warned off the project, which was believed by many to be unfeasible, but it was rescued with support from the new Director, Royal Armoured Corps, General Raymond Briggs and Claude Gibb at the Ministry of Supply. The new scheme involved mounting the gun, with its recoil mechanism, on raised trunnions and cutting a hole in the back of the turret, which was fitted with an armoured box that not only served as a counterweight but also housed the wireless set which, otherwise, would have been smashed to

93 *The prototype 17-pounder installation on a Sherman V at Chertsey. The new loader's hatch can be seen, as well as the wireless set in its armoured extension at the back of the turret.*

pieces by the recoil action of the gun. An extra hatch aperture was cut into the turret roof for the loader, making it easier to get the longer ammunition into the turret. Firing trials proved that the mounting was perfectly satisfactory at all angles, but there were still problems.

Excessive flash occurred at the muzzle, which made accurate firing difficult, but worse still was flashback at the breech end, which unnerved and even scorched the crew. Witheridge was called in again to advise, because the best idea anyone else had come up with was that of kitting out the crew with asbestos gauntlets and hoods, like those worn by naval gun-crews. Witheridge advised delaying the action of the semi-automatic breech, which solved the problem, and he also recommended turning the breech block through ninety degrees, making it easier to load the long rounds in such a tight space. The problem of obscuration by muzzle flash was never entirely solved, but when the final, successful firing trials took place in February 1944 the decision had already been taken, on 30 December 1943, to order 2,100 Shermans of the M4A4 type to be converted at the Royal Ordnance Factory at Barnbow near Leeds. In addition to turret modifications, each tank had the hull gunner's position removed and the machine-gun aperture plated over in order to provide stowage for fifteen rounds of ammunition, while capacity was found for another sixty-three rounds in and beneath the turret basket. In this way, and almost unofficially, Britain was furnished with the best tank in the entire Western Allied arsenal, and the only one capable of taking on German Panthers and Tigers more or less on their own terms.

In the summer of 1943 an unusual experiment was sponsored by the School of Infantry as a means of dealing with anti-tank guns. Experience had shown that the most dangerous time for tanks in a direct assault was the short period between the lifting of a barrage on the enemy's forward positions and the arrival of tanks. During that interval the gunners had enough time to scramble out of their slit trenches and man their weapons before the tanks got among them. It followed that the infantry suffered too, because their worst enemies, the German machine-gunners, also had a breathing space in which to prepare. The argument was that the barrage should be there to assist the infantry, and if it was found possible to operate tanks safely where the shells were falling, much would be gained. Under normal circumstances the first indication a tank has of an anti-tank gun is the flash it makes when firing, which is often too late. If, it was argued, the tanks could move around in the impact area they could destroy the guns while they were still unmanned, always assuming they could locate them. This was the object of the trial.

A squadron of sixteen Churchills was used, supported by three field regiments of 25-pounders – seventy-two guns. In the first trial, firing at the reduced rate of one round per gun per minute, one tank suffered a broken track and another some bogie damage, but there were no crew casualties and commanders reported no difficulty in locating and engaging targets.

For the second trial the intensity of fire was doubled, to the normal rate, and the tanks spent five minutes cruising around in the fire-swept zone without any problems at all.

This was some tribute to the resilience of the Churchill, although standard high explosive rounds were used instead of air bursts which the gunners would normally have employed, because these risked damaging the tanks' air inlets. It was also admitted that the ground had a lot to do with it. If it was dry, dusty or sandy, the chances were that tanks moving through the barrage would not be able to see a thing.

The foregoing account is but one example of the nature of direct assault tactics, the original *raison d'être* of the tank, which the heavily protected infantry tank had been designed to fulfil. What, then, was an Assault Tank? The answer is that nobody seemed to know for certain. The type came about through what appears to have been some rather woolly thinking on the part of tank manufacturers and others, outside the normal circle of tank design, who believed that they knew best – a familiar state of affairs in Britain, if past experience is anything to go by. Many tank pundits regarded it as a contradiction in terms, an offensive weapon designed and built around defensive principles, for with one extreme exception, every assault tank built had armament to normal tank standards, behind very thick armour. In a sense the concept had been foreshadowed in the massive A20 and TOG designs of 1940 but in terms of size the new generation were tiny, and intended to be.

In August 1942, when the Churchill tank had shown every sign of being a lame duck, the Defence Committee, in conjunction with the Secretary of State for War and Minister of Supply, had agreed that Vauxhall Motors should turn over to production of the Cromwell tank in the summer of 1943. As with all good intentions, this was soon watered down to the stage where the firm would produce drawings for a tank very similar to the Cromwell 'in which it had faith', suggesting that anything designed elsewhere could not be trusted. This was agreed because, although it meant a two-month delay in starting, it apparently guaranteed a better product. Vauxhall's improved Cromwell is mentioned elsewhere, but the firm also suggested to the General Staff that they should produce a more heavily armoured tank, presumably on the grounds that they could retain an interest in infantry tank production when the Churchill was abandoned. The result, given the General Staff specification A31, was described as an all-welded Cromwell hull with side skirts supporting a Churchill type composite turret; a tank with an estimated weight of 32 tons. In passing, it is worth noting that a design also exists called A28; of unknown origin, it approaches the problem from the other end by creating an infantry tank based on A27 (Centaur/Cromwell) components which must have looked very similar to the Vauxhall offering, but for the Cromwell-style turret. At about the same time, the English Electric Company in Stafford was asked to design the A32, described as a heavy assault tank project 'while Vauxhall design an interim assault tank . . . successor to Churchill'.

In the United States meanwhile, the American Locomotive Company had been building an assault tank under the designation T14, to the order of the British Tank Mission from a design schemed out at Aberdeen Proving Ground in Maryland. It was now agreed that both English Electric and American Locomotive should produce two prototypes, one of each for evaluation in each country, with the English Electric design taking the General Staff specification A33 (A28, A31 and A32 having now been discontinued).

Since it had been under discussion since March 1942, T14 was completed first. It was based largely on Sherman components with the Ford V8 engine, although an option was taken on the V12 when that was ready. Conforming with standard American practice the hull was built out over the tracks to accommodate all stowage internally, although unlike the Sherman, T14 had sloping side armour in addition to the front. Taking advantage of this slope the armour, which was 100-mm on the nose, reduced to 50-mm higher up and, as a concession to British requirements, the tank had side skirting panels to protect the suspension. The turret ring was identical to that of the Sherman, and naturally the 75-mm gun was fitted, although it was planned to replace this with the 76-mm when that became available. In October 1943 one source claimed the tank was capable of mounting a 90-mm weapon, although how this was supposed to fit the existing turret ring, which could hardly be expanded, is not explained. By December, however, the 42-ton T14 project

94 *The chunky-looking T14 Assault Tank designed in the USA to British requirements.*

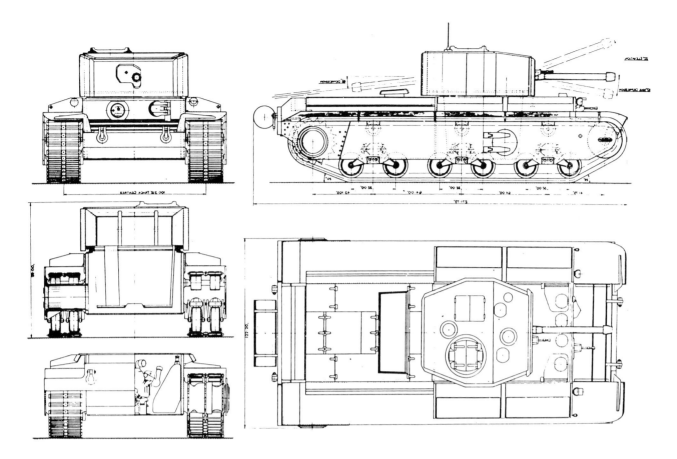

Drawing I: *Plans of the English Electric A33 Tank Excelsior.*

was described as 'virtually dead' in the United States since the advent of the T26, but one prototype was certainly shipped to Britain for trials, because it is still here.

English Electric's A33, which was apparently christened Excelsior at one stage, although it didn't excel at anything, finally appeared in two forms. Pilot A featured a suspension system based on the American T1 heavy tank while Pilot B employed the RL suspension, developed by Rolls-Royce and the LMS Railway, which worked on a sort of scissors action with helical springs. A Pilot C, with what was described as a 'light RL suspension' was not proceeded with. In most other respects both tanks were near enough identical. The hull was very much Cromwell in outline and naturally the Meteor engine and Merritt-Brown transmission were employed, while the turret also followed the familiar outline. Pilot A carried a 6-pounder and Pilot B the British 75-mm, with the respectable armour thickness of 4.5 in. (114 mm) on all vertical front surfaces. Both pilots had skirting plates, with dreadfully cramped crew escape hatches in them but only on Pilot B was the top run of the track totally enclosed. At one stage there was talk of increasing the frontal armour to 6 in. (152 mm) and fitting the high-velocity 75-mm gun, although again this seems rather optimistic for a tank with a 57-in. turret ring. This may have been one response to a

comment which claimed that there was no tactical use for a tank that weighed 40 tons but only mounted a 6-pounder gun, although if that were true it might apply to Churchill just as well. In November 1943 Pilot A began its acceptance trials, loaded to its battle weight of 40 tons 8 cwt, with a 1,000 mile run based on Stafford. Across country it managed to pick up two extra tons of mud, although it was described as highly reliable, yet a second 1,000 mile trial virtually wrote it off. Pilot B, described as almost complete on 23 December 1943, was criticised for its suspension on the grounds that it was too complex, but it seems that by the time it was finished, the A33 project was as good as dead.

Another contender for the ideal assault tank was A38, which they named Valiant. Here, it seems, there was a different emphasis since thick armour was to be combined with the lowest possible weight, which obviously implied a very small tank. To that extent the designers succeeded, since 114-mm frontal armour was available on a tank that only weighed 27 tons. A report dated December 1943 explained that three prototypes would be built, with an entirely new (low weight) suspension, of a small, heavily armoured tank for the Far East. Vickers appear to have dropped the project at an early stage, passing it on to Birmingham Railway Carriage & Wagon, but it finished up with Ruston Hornsby who completed one prototype in 1944. The construction technique was not unlike that of the Matilda, with large castings bolted together internally, but the designers paid a terrible price for the weight concession. The rear end of the hull was only 9 in. off the ground, making it liable to foul even the smallest bump, while each suspension unit, with its independent wishbone arms and lubrication pipe, was an open invitation to snag and damage on undergrowth – a distinct liability in Far Eastern jungles. Powered by a General Motors two-stroke diesel rated at 210 hp, the Valiant was also underpowered, with a top speed of only 12 mph, and it gave the appearance of being weighed down by its turret, which could take the 6-pounder or 75-mm gun.

95   *The much-abused A38 Valiant at Chertsey. The small, cast nose section gives some indication of the cramped driver's position.*

The report that killed off Valiant was issued by the Fighting Vehicle Proving Establishment at Chertsey, where the tank had gone for suspension performance trials. These had ended prematurely, and the report, dated 7 May 1945, was a classic. On the first day the tank had gone a mere thirteen miles by road when an oil leak had been suspected. It was towed back to Chertsey, where it was discovered that the oil tank had been overfilled. There was nothing wrong with Valiant. However, the driver reported that thirteen miles was quite enough for him; he was exhausted. Tests revealed that a pull of between 140 and 160 pounds was necessary to operate the steering levers, and there was worse to come: releasing the foot-brake, according to Chertsey, was not humanly possible since the pedal was in such a position that it could only be worked by the driver's heel, and if he did manage to shift it there was a fair chance of his foot becoming trapped between the pedal and the floorplate, which could lead to serious injury. The gear lever was no better. In first gear it came to rest behind the batteries and once in position could only be disengaged with the aid of a crowbar. In fifth gear, on the other hand, it was so close to the right steering lever, which came back with considerable force, that the driver was in danger of breaking his wrist. Even

assuming he survived these little inconveniences, the driver was still likely to be crippled for life by his seat. It was described as uncomfortable in both the lowered and the raised positions – in the former the poor man was forced to crouch, nearly bent double, and in the latter he stood a good chance of injuring himself on the edge of the hatch. There is more: indeed it is quite surprising just how much condemnation can be squeezed into three pages of sober commentary, but it need not detain us. The officer in charge of the field trials admitted that his brief had only extended to a report on the tank's suspension, but he had decided to abandon the trials because it was neither possible, nor safe, to continue and in his view the entire project should be closed. It was, but even that wasn't the end of Valiant. The tank was retained by the School of Tank Technology, where it became a star turn after the war. At the end of every course the students were lined up while Valiant trundled by and they were then invited to crawl all over it and compile a list of the design faults they could discover. One hopes they started early in the morning.

In February 1944 there were reports of a Heavy Valiant, which might well have been the same as the Valiant II mentioned late in 1943. It was described as being essentially a Valiant turret and hull front married to an A33 hull with the T1-type suspension. The armour was given as 10 in. thick on the turret and 9 in. on the hull front, yet the weight was calculated at 42.25 tons, so the tank must have been quite small. It was to have been powered by the new 400-hp Meteorite V8 driving through a Rolls-Royce five-speed synchromesh gearbox and controlled epicyclic steering system. Armament was to be either the 6-pounder, 75-mm or 95-mm options, or a multiple machine-gun turret, with a total crew of three. The multiple machine-gun turret does not appear to have been intended for anti-aircraft use, because a similar arrangement was planned for the Churchill. A brief item in a report dated 23 November 1943 speaks of a Heavy Churchill (the A22F Mark VII type) mounting multiple 20-mm weapons for use against ground targets. Proof that this was not just a drawing board project can be found in another report of January 1945 which claims that the prototype had been taken down from Cheshunt to Lulworth for firing trials. Evidently nothing came of it, although to date no photograph or drawing has been found to show what it looked like.

That the assault tank was not simply a British aberration can be shown by reference to the heavily uparmoured Sherman variant which entered service with the United States Army, or the various German and Soviet designs generally classed as assault guns; that is turretless fighting vehicles, usually well armoured and with the gun in a limited traverse mounting at the front. The respective advantages of a turret or fixed gun exercised the minds of British designers for a machine described as providing close support of infantry and in April 1943 some suitably vague statements were made regarding a small, heavily armoured, special purpose vehicle which was to have the 'optimum combination of armour and armament' – something, one supposes, that every tank designer was looking for. Indeed such platitudes could be applied to all the assault tanks, but in this instance the subject was a design then being worked out by Nuffield Mechanizations Ltd in Birmingham. Their first proposal, dated 13 May 1943, was along much the same lines as the original Valiant, and may well have been prepared to meet the same specification, yet six days later they offered something quite different. In fact by 5 October 1943 they had submitted a total of sixteen designs, each bigger and heavier than the last. Known to the firm as the AT (Assault Tank) series, only the first was turreted, at least in the conventional sense. After that, designs appeared at the astounding rate of two or three a month with almost every combination of armament imaginable, from multiple machine-guns in little turrets with flamethrowers and mortars to 6-pounder, and from AT13 onwards, 17-pounder guns. Frontal armour increased from 6 to 9 in. over the same period, until AT15A was estimated as weighing 65 tons.

Although there is a wealth of surviving documentation, it is not clear who might have been the driving force behind this extraordinary effort. Lord Nuffield is an obvious contender, but all the dealings between his company and the Ministry of Supply were conducted by Sir Miles Thomas.

It is not even possible to say how many of the proposals ever reached the authorities, or were rejected by them, although the suspicion must be that most never left Birmingham. The only reference discovered in the Tank Board minutes is dated 23 December 1943, stating that the

design (presumably AT15A) was not justified at 68 (*sic*) tons with a 17-pounder gun; rather the 3.7-in. weapon was suggested. Quite when the War Office first got involved is not known, but some unguarded comments in contemporary documents suggest that the Nuffield project was a particular favourite of the Secretary of State for War Mr Duncan Sandys, who was the Prime Minister's son-in-law. It was just the sort of project Winston Churchill revelled in. TOG and Nellie* might have gone to the wall, but here was a new leviathan. Design AT16, which was submitted on 5 February 1944, showed the 3.7-in. anti-aircraft gun (now referred to as the 37-pounder) protruding from the centre of a large cast housing, 9 in. thick at the front, to produce a vehicle with an estimated weight of 72 tons. With some modifications it was accepted under the apt name of Tortoise with the General Staff specification A39. When Tortoise came in, all the restrictions that had hitherto cramped the style of British tank designers went straight out of the window. Considerations of rail movement, road transportation and the width of Bailey bridges or landing craft ramps were simply ignored; one feels that such disregard could only have been exercised at the highest level; perhaps Duncan Sandys, backed by his father-in-law?

An order for twenty-five machines, first placed in February 1944, was confirmed in May with delivery expected from September 1945 on condition that this was a production order; no prototypes. We are back on familiar ground again. In this case, however, disaster was averted by the long development period. When none had

---

* D J Fletcher, *The Great Tank Scandal*, HMSO, 1989, pp 22–6.

96   *The original A39 Tortoise prototype P1, on a Pickfords low loader in charge of Diamond T and Scammell tractors.*

appeared that September, with the war already over, the order was reduced to twelve and in the following year it was halved again; ultimately, only five were built. A complete Tortoise weighed 78 tons, only 2 tons less than TOG, and the gun was modified to fire a 32-pound round, which was calculated to give a better performance than the projected 37-pounder. It was powered by the Meteor/ Merritt-Brown combination and had a top speed of 12 mph, riding on a curious double torsion bar suspension with massive 36-in. wide tracks. Post-war trials proved that Tortoise was a nightmare to transport anywhere, although it was surprisingly reliable for such a novel design and was an excellent gun platform, especially for the 32-pounder, which turned out to be a supremely accurate and hard-hitting weapon. Among its more unusual features the actual gun mounting is worthy of note, since the barrel protruded through a vast ball-like arrangement rather than the usual trunnions. The secondary armament, a throwback to some of the earlier designs, included a pair of Besa machine-guns in a rotating cupola on top of the hull. Since there was every chance that these weapons, fired indiscriminately in the heat of the moment, could have swept off most of the hull fittings – or the head of any other crew member unlucky enough to be looking out of a hatch at the time – a series of stops were incorporated in the firing mechanism to prevent this.

Sir Miles Thomas tells a story of the first Tortoise's first steps. He was given the honour of piloting it out of the shed where it had been completed and, in lining it up on the exit door he pulled back on the left stick, only to have the tank, to his horror, start to swing right, in the direction of the door post. Fortunately the huge tank was stopped in time and, according to the raconteur – who was far too important to make a silly mistake in pulling the wrong lever – the sticks had been connected up the wrong way round which, to be fair, from the look of them would not have been impossible.

Whatever else they might have been accused of, nobody could say that the Nuffield Organisation ever gave up. In 1944 they came up with a new tank engine, presumably with the intention of keeping the dreaded Meteor at bay. Known as the Democrat (which implies an American connection), it was described by FVPE as being similar to the Liberty Mark V, except that it had enclosed rocker gear, redesigned pistons and a new clutch. Two were tested in Centaur hulls at Chertsey in September 1944. No horsepower rating is given, although some minor defects were noticed, but the type was never adopted. A year earlier, another Centaur hull had been used to test a version of the Rolls-Royce Meteorite, built by the Austin Motor Company. This was a 400-hp V8 which, according to FVPE, fitted very well into the tank, but a main bearing failure put an end to that trial.

By the time that the Second Front was being seriously considered, when Britain was irrevocably committed to the Cromwell for at least some of its armoured regiments,

it was important to ensure that they were produced to a standard that was operationally acceptable. To that end, on 2 February 1944, Leyland Motors issued a detailed specification for what they described as the Battle Cromwell. In the main this concerned itself with mechanical components and laid down the exact type of Meteor engine and Merritt Brown transmission that had been proved to give the most reliable performance. Apart from a few 95-mm gun models, all those designated for active service were of the Mark IV and Mark V types, mounting the 75-mm gun. Ever since it had first been installed there had been trouble with the Vickers-designed elevating gear, which was so slack that it made accurate shooting impossible. A revised pattern was now available and Leylands announced that any tanks still equipped with the old type which were otherwise satisfactory, would be visited by a flying squad of engineers equipped to exchange it. In order to improve the Cromwell's resistance to mines an extra panel of 6-mm armour was to be fitted to the 8-mm floor plate below the crew compartment. All major riveted joints in the front hull structure would be strengthened with seam welding, which would also have the advantage of increasing the tank's resistance to water during wading, and welding would also be used to improve the attachment of outer turret skin plates.

The next obvious step was to adopt welding as the main method of construction. Plans were drawn up in 1943 and by April of the following year BRC&W were able to report eighty-two completed from an order for 160. In these tanks a new hull floor was provided beneath the crew compartments made from a single 14-mm plate. Other modifications included a sideways-opening escape hatch for the hull gunner and twin smoke-dischargers mounted on the back plate. Tanks of this type were classified as Mark Vw. With subsequent developments in mind, Leylands also produced a version of Cromwell known as Pilot D. The purpose was to prepare modifications which would be required when extra armour brought the tank's weight up to 30 tons. The most obvious step was to produce stronger springs and improved shock absorbers, but wider (15½-in. instead of 14-in.) tracks were considered, while the roadwheels were fitted with Avon solid tyres that did not have the perforations seen on earlier Christie cruisers. This work proved particularly useful when design work began on the A34 Comet. Another development of the welded Cromwell was an uparmoured version apparently produced by Rolls-Royce, for a report was issued under their name in August 1943 on what they described as the Cromwell Appliqué. This term was used to indicate that the extra armour was simply welded on to the original hull and turret, wherever it would fit. The result, compared with a typical Cromwell of the same period, was an increase in frontal armour from 64 mm to 101 mm on the hull and from 76 mm to 101 mm on the turret. Since a welded Cromwell was about half a ton lighter than a riveted one, this appliqué version was, overall, only about

97　*The special Rolls-Royce Cromwell displaying its array of appliqué armour.*

a quarter of a ton heavier than the latter type. Even so, it was pointed out that when the heavier Cromwell suspension became available, that should be fitted. Photographs of the tank show clearly where the extra armour was to go, and of course it had to be cut carefully to fit around the driver's visor and hull machine-gun mounting, which could not be thickened. In Stage II, appliqué armour would be used to increase the thickness of the hull sides from 32 mm to about 35 mm and the turret sides from 63 mm to 75 mm. In this form the estimated total weight would have been just over 29 tons, although that would include strengthened suspension components, wider road-wheels and the 15½-in. track. No estimate was given on how this might affect performance but, welcome as extra armour always is, nothing more could be done to improve firepower, and that would seem to have been a much more pressing requirement.

It may be asked why, instead of slapping more armour on to existing vertical surfaces, some attempt was not made to design sloped armour for British tanks? The Sherman had this feature, on the front at least, while the Soviet T-34 and German Panther were renowned for it. Certainly most crews believed in it, and anyone who had wriggled out of his Sherman to see where an 88-mm round had gouged out a lump of armour as it glanced off, where it ought to have penetrated and killed him, was obviously going to be difficult to convince otherwise. A sober appraisal of the respective advantages was laid out in a brief discussion paper by Colonel F W Gordon-Hall and,

as we have already seen, what that officer said on tank design generally deserved to be taken seriously. Gordon-Hall stated that the first duty of any tank designer was to enclose the vital parts of a tank with a suit of armour in which no internal space was wasted. The ideal shape, he suggested, was a sphere, but in practical terms it had to be a box because major components such as the engine, transmission and fighting compartments formed natural rectangular blocks. Taking the basic plate to be 100-mm thick, he showed that similar protection could be obtained from a plate sloped at 30 degrees which was 80-mm thick. However, this would have a greater surface area, also enclosing some inessential space, so the weight saving would be minimal.

As for the assumption that angled plates deflect shot, Gordon-Hall pointed out that this depended on the shape of the armour-piercing projectile, but that in any case this was only likely to happen at angles of slope between 40 and 55 degrees. Against 30-degree plate, the accepted norm, the shot would tend to turn inwards on striking, rather than glance off. In pursuing this, one is liable to become trapped in the heady realms of higher mathematics, and the Colonel's intention was to keep it simple enough for ordinary mortals to comprehend while also, no doubt, stirring up some discussion. He pointed out, for instance, that unless the ground was entirely level, two tanks engaged in a firefight could be at different elevations, in which the advantage of angled plate might be entirely negated. What he did not mention was that even a tank built all of vertical plates on a flat surface could meet its enemy obliquely and thus achieve the effect of angled plate in relation to a strike. His conclusion was that vertical plate would always give at least its designed performance, whereas angled plate could not be relied upon because it depended very much on the angle of attack.

It would be wrong to assume from this that British tank designers were actually a lot more sensible than their foreign counterparts. Enough has already been written to suggest that expediency had as much to do with it as expertise, but Colonel Gordon-Hall's paper is an interesting challenge to accepted views both then and since.

By 1944 the Rotatrailer had almost slipped into merciful oblivion. Before D-Day some were allocated to a curious Allied unit charged with assisting French farmers after the invasion but, as far as the tanks were concerned, they had gone. Only the idea remained, and it reappeared in 1944 as the High Speed Trailer. It was built by Ernest Wright Ltd of Wolverhampton as a two-wheeled trailer running on pneumatic tyred wheels which were mounted on a pair of Cromwell (i.e. Christie) suspension units. It was designed for use with Cromwells and, as the designers pointed out, in an emergency the tank could repair itself from trailer components. The need for carrying fuel having been dropped, the trailer was designed to stow two tons of ammunition, 6-pounder and 17-pounder rounds being specified, along with some of the stowage normally attached to the outside of the tank. It was fully enclosed, but because the suspension could take the weight, was also armoured against 20-mm cannon fire. After a 200 mile cross-country trial behind a Cromwell the ammunition stored inside was all found to be in perfect condition and the equipment was adopted as Armoured Trailer No 1, Mark I, although there is no evidence of its ever being used in service.

98 *The Armoured Trailer with all its hatches open to display the internal arrangements. It even has some spare track links stowed on the mudguards.*

An agreement to open a new front in northern Europe was taken in Washington in the spring of 1943 and the nucleus of an invasion force formed as 21st Army Group. Its first Commander-in-Chief, Sir Bernard Paget, was appointed in June. A month later he was writing to the Deputy Chief of the Imperial General Staff, General Sir Ronald Weeks, on the subject of tank armament. He made the point that Britain was badly behind the Germans in this field and quoted penetration figures for the 75-mm gun in the Panther compared with the same calibre weapon in the Sherman and the 6-pounder in the Cromwell. This was a serious handicap to the Allies, who were outranged and were obliged to make the best possible use of ground in the attack. The Germans, on the other hand, could afford to reduce the armour thickness of their tanks as long as their guns kept ours at a respectful distance. He requested that efforts be made, as he put it, to 'pop up' the muzzle velocity of the Sherman's 75-mm until it was in line with that of Panther, but he also wanted a new gun which was better than the German 88-mm – something capable of penetrating 150 mm of armour at 1,500 yards. This, he explained, would allow for future German developments and offset the difference he perceived between the quality of German face-hardened armour against the homogeneous type used by the Allies.

The DCIGS waited until early October before replying, beginning diplomatically by saying that he could not agree more with Sir Bernard. He discussed the 17-pounder, but claimed that the General Staff wanted to go beyond even that and mentioned the proposed 3.7-in. high-velocity gun. He went on to say that experiments to install the 17-pounder in the Sherman looked promising, but regretted that it would never be a high-class, high-explosive weapon and he pointed out that any high-velocity anti-tank weapon which was also expected to fire HE effectively would require dual dials on the elevating handwheel and separate range tables for each type of projectile. In essence, it seems the C-in-C was being told to wait and see.

For the thousands of tank crewmen, working frantically to prepare their Shermans, Churchills and Cromwells for the forthcoming struggle against a cornered Wehrmacht in continental Europe, wait and see was all they could do. Concepts like Tortoise were just fantasy. The real world consisted of rather dated but, at long last, reliable tanks forged in a four-year struggle with the military establishment and industry. These tanks, inferior on a one-for-one basis with the best their enemy could field, were at least available in quantities that the Germans could never match, and therein lay their strength. For the present, all that mattered was to get them ready for a short wade through shallow water from landing craft to beach. What happened after that was in the lap of the gods, aided and abetted by the generals.

One factor that augered well for the tanks, particularly in the early stages of an assault landing, was the strong commitment to specialised armour. By early 1944 most of the equipment destined to be used on D-Day and beyond was either in service or at least in advanced stages of development, but this did not mean that evolution would freeze at a given point. Further progress with the DD tank has already been noted, and the same was true of the Sherman Crab.

Trials with the original Crab had shown that on rough, undulating ground there was a tendency for the flails to pass over some mines if the tank was pitched at the wrong angle, so some thought was given to allowing the flail jib to move independently of the tank. Following experiments with the Sherman Marquis prototype, AEC Ltd devised what became known as the Contouring Crab. Tests had shown that an effect known as flail reaction caused a free-floating jib to assume the best flailing height under most circumstances, so the hydraulic lifting gear was removed from the nearside arm, to the rear of which a counterweight was added. A locking device was still incorporated, otherwise the flail would not work against wire, but on trials over irregular ground a Contouring Crab returned a 90 per cent destruction rate, as against 65 per cent for the original model. It was adopted in May 1944 and subsequently entered service as the Crab II.

Yet even this did not solve all problems. When faced with a steep slope a Crab's flailing ability decreased as more torque was used up in climbing, because a Contouring Crab had the adverse effect of lowering its jib as the tank climbed. The initial response to this was based upon American experiments with their huge Aunt Jemima rollers, which was to employ what in railway parlance would be called a banking engine. A large bumper plate was fitted to the rear of a Crab II, against which another

Sherman would push. An ordinary Sherman V was used in the trial. It did not work. The pushing tank developed serious track slip and therefore failed to provide much extra traction, and it tended to wander off course. Even if it had worked, there was an equal and opposite problem which could not be resolved. As it tended to dig in going uphill, so a Contouring Crab generally flailed fresh air going downhill, and no amount of pushing or pulling could prevent that. The final solution came in the form of an auxiliary gearbox. AEC again masterminded the experiment, using in the first instance one of their Mammoth Major truck gearboxes interposed between the tank's engine and the flail drive. This enabled the flailing speed to be maintained even if the tank was slowed down by steep hills or sticky ground. In the final version, which was introduced for Crabs I and II in February 1945, an Albion gearbox was employed.

Two other problems associated with mechanical mine clearance were station-keeping and lane-marking. The former was a matter of getting two flails to run accurately in echelon across a minefield without wandering away from each other and leaving unswept gaps. As a problem it was of most concern to the following tank which, besides being under fire and having its own mines to contend with, needed to keep accurate station on its leader in a dust cloud whipped up by the flails and debris from exploding mines. In its simplest form a station-keeping indicator was a tall pole at the back of the leading tank; at its most sophisticated it was a device linking the two tanks by cable which showed each driver the relative angle and distance of his mate. This worked remarkably well under test conditions, but the nature of the equipment was too

99 *A Sherman Crab II, viewed from the rear to show the station-keeping arms and the two angled boxes that dispense lane markers.*

susceptible to mine blast for it to be used on service. Lane-marking, that is leaving something on the ground to indicate the swept path, ran the gamut of devices that trickled chalk from a box, to spiked rollers and attachments which fired flags into the ground at regular intervals. Most such devices worked well enough in good conditions but, being vulnerable, were always liable to be knocked or shot off a tank in action.

While flail development progressed to an impressively high standard, there were still those who expected to achieve more by the process of sympathetic detonation. Based on what the Scorpion regiment had already done in Italy, they developed the flying Bangalore torpedo idea. In its simplest form, used operationally, it consisted of two launcher tubes on each arm of a CIRD attachment, from which Bangalores could be fired into minefields or wire entanglements and detonated. Similar clusters of tubes were also mounted on the trackguards of Churchill AVREs. Without doubt, however, the doyen of all these variations was Wurlitzer. The prototype was based on a redundant Churchill 3-in. gun carrier with the armament removed. A bank of twenty-five Bangalore tubes was mounted on each trackguard in five layers of five. Each one could launch a 3-in., 2-ft long Bangalore to a distance of 16 ft in front of the vehicle which, exploding in the air, would clear a 12-ft wide path through a field of Tellermines. In June 1944 it was claimed that the prototype was being redesigned, and in their final report 79th Armoured Division confirmed that it was worth developing further, although there is no indication that it was ever used in action.

In January 1944 another device was developed, equally applicable to Sherman or Churchill although, for obvious reasons, normally used with the Churchill AVRE. This was Conger which, like its namesake, was dangerous to anyone who came near it, friend or foe. Conger consisted of 330 yards of specially woven 2-in. hosepiping, which could be launched across a minefield by a 5-in. rocket. The equipment was mounted inside a redundant Universal Carrier which was first stripped of all its internal fittings, including the engine. Thus it was towed behind a tank and positioned at the edge of the minefield. The rocket apparatus was fitted to the Carrier while the hose was carefully flaked down inside. Prior to an operation the hose had to be soaked in water for twelve hours, otherwise it would leak. The rocket was fired, and it sailed away across the minefield carrying the hose behind it. Now came the tricky bit. The hose was pumped full with 2,500 pounds of liquid explosive 822C, under compressed air, and then detonated, if the volatile stuff had not chosen to go off already of its own accord. This is what occured when it was used in Normandy, and the premature explosion caused such devastation that it got a very bad name for itself.

Once a minefield is located it can be dealt with in a variety of ways, but the mine's great advantage is surprise.

100 The mighty Wurlitzer, an erstwhile Churchill 3-in. gun carrier mounting fifty explosive tubes for mine-clearing.

101 The volatile Conger in a gutted Universal Carrier, towed behind a Churchill AVRE.

102 Sherman with Lulu mine-detection equipment. In this view the wooden arms and rollers are displayed in the stowed position.

Finding it with tank propelled rollers was one way of destroying this advantage, but the mine wreaked its revenge on the roller. Electronic detection was another way, but this meant that vulnerable sappers had to precede the tanks on foot, unless a tank-mounted device could be

103   Bantu, mounted on Staghound, with the detectors extended, but still in the travelling position.

created. Such a thing was devised in the first half of 1944, and mounted on a Sherman; it enjoyed the codename Lulu. The detection apparatus consisted of an electrical coil, sensitive to metal, which was obviously a difficult thing to use near a tank. For this reason it was enclosed within a large wooden drum which a contemporary report describes as having been 'Bakelized' – not a word one might expect to find in a modern dictionary, but presumed to derive from Bakelite, an early resin-based plastic which in this case, it seems, was impregnated into the wood. The drum was suspended from a lightweight lattice girder arm, also made from Bakelized wood, so that the first metal fittings one came across were the brackets which attached it to the tank. In fact there were three of these arms and drums on the tank, two at the front, covering the tracks, and another at the back which scanned the gap between the tracks. In the stowed position, the tank's turret was enveloped in enormous rollers but the three arms, activated automatically by the driver, swung out in a lazy away until they rested gently on the ground. The tank moved forwards very slowly and when one roller passed over a mine a loud buzzer sounded, causing the driver to stop. He then scanned a bank of three lights adjacent to the instrument panel, and from this decided which roller the mine was under. Appropriate action was then taken to lift it. The drawbacks were numerous: the detector could not distinguish between mines and any other bit of metal, so a good deal of time was wasted digging up scrap. Then again, once a real mine was found, unprotected sappers had to come and make it safe, possibly under fire. Lulu could not have worked in conjunction with mine-clearing tanks, because the amount of shunting about which would have been necessary for another tank to get near the located mine, without it or Lulu coming to grief on another one, would have been an invitation to disaster on a battlefield. Similar equipment on a Staghound armoured car was called Bantu. Six prototypes of each were built and issued to the Royal Armoured Corps for troop trials, but no production orders were ever placed.

During the desert war the British had developed Command Tanks, which looked outwardly like any other, but with ammunition removed and a dummy gun installed to make room for extra wireless equipment, enabling regimental commanders to keep up with their tanks and yet remain in touch with their own headquarters and higher echelons. Most were local improvisations, which gradually grew in sophistication to the point where at least one armoured division, destined for Italy but unwilling to part with its roomy Grant command tank, had it disguised to look like an overgrown Sherman.

By 1943 the system had become regularised to the extent that a whole programme was worked out in Britain to cover all eventualities. This covered four classes of such vehicles. These were Command, Control, Rear Link and Observation Post. This last, being a Royal Artillery related type, need not concern us here but the other three all deserve some attention. Command tanks or armoured cars were top of the tree. They were issued to divisional and brigade headquarters and contained two No 19 wireless sets, one High Power (HP) one Low Power (LP), which linked them to army and regimental nets. With one exception – the Sherman Command Type B – they had the main armament and ammunition removed. There were command versions of Sherman, Cromwell and Staghound, while Churchills were being developed for the Far East. Control tanks and armoured cars came next. They served the same purpose at armoured regiment and armoured reconnaissance regiment level. They carried two No 19 LP sets and a No 38 set but retained their armament and ammunition where possible. They were available in Sherman, Cromwell, Churchill and Staghound, to suit what their regiment employed. Rear Link tanks and armoured cars were essentially relay stations and carried one No 19 HP set and sometimes a No 38 as well. Sherman and Cromwell Rear Links retained their armament and ammunition, while the Humber armoured car version already described did not.

7 Liberation

104 *Deep-wading trials off Weymouth, Two Stuart VI (M5A1) light tanks at turret-depth with air-intakes erected and waterproofing over the mantlet. The driver works entirely on instructions from the commander.*

Although many military operations had an appointed D-day and an H-hour when they were due to commence, history only recognises one D-Day: 6 June 1944. The initial footprint upon alien sand is significant, but it is no guarantee of success. With its means of retreat cut off, the invading force is highly vulnerable until it can secure a deep beach-head, and vast reserves are essential in order to maintain the pressure for a long period. What goes on in the front line is crucial, but it is only so much pointless sacrifice unless constant and substantial support can be assured. For example, if one looks at the armoured element of the British Second and Canadian First Armies at the time of Overlord, they comprised six armoured divisions – one of which was Polish – and nine independent armoured brigades: roughly 2,250 tanks, not including other vehicles. Obviously they could not all land on one day, but numbers increased steadily over the first six weeks and they had to be backed up. Consequently, until an operational rear maintenance area could be established to repair breakdowns or battle damage and hold an adequate reserve stock of tanks on French soil, the General Staff required that quantities of tanks should be available in Britain for immediate despatch. They calculated that this reserve should represent 25 per cent of the unit establishment, which meant a constant stock, not counting casualties, of some 3,000 tanks, and a constant stock meant continual maintenance of the reserve from primary sources. To the Americans this attitude smacked

of British conservatism, but it paid dividends in due course.

Most, if not all, of these tanks would be shipped across the Channel in landing craft and driven ashore across open beaches, so they all had to be waterproofed. This work was carried out at unit level and involved the sealing, with various plastic compounds, of every vulnerable orifice against the ingress of water, and the fitting of special deep-wading kits. These were manufactured as Flatpacks, delivered in dismantled form, which fitted over the air intakes and exhaust outlets of vehicles enabling them to operate in moderately deep water without drowning their engines. Since the progress of opening-up port facilities on the French coast could not be forecast in detail it was decreed that all vehicles landed up to D+42 (18 July) should be waterproofed; this in itself was a massive commitment in terms of time, manpower and material.

On D-Day itself almost all the armour that came ashore over the Normandy beaches in the British sector belonged to the specialist 79th Armoured Division, but in keeping with the pattern this will be discussed at the end of the chapter. Among the few exceptions was the Royal Marines Assault Regiment. This had been formed originally with the purpose of providing fire support from the sea for Royal Marine Commandos operating at specified locations on the British and Canadian beaches. The idea was that the tanks, 95-mm gun Centaurs and a few Shermans in the command role, would be shackled to the decks of tank

105   A close support Centaur of the Royal Marines Armoured Support Group on a highway south of Bayeux in Normandy on 10 June 1944.

landing craft from which they could fire during the run in. The landing craft would then beach themselves, while the tanks brought down supporting fire as required until such time as the field artillery was ashore and ready to take over. Since it was not intended to take the tanks ashore, no drivers were included in the crews and to make absolutely sure, the engines were lifted out, leaving more room for ammunition. Having trained in this role, and developed an unusual gunnery technique to suit, which will be described later, the unit took part in a demonstration operation, Exercise Savvy, apparently at Studland Bay in Dorset, which was witnessed by His Majesty King George VI and General Montgomery. It all went off well enough but Monty was constrained to remark that, having got the tanks thus far, it seemed a shame that they should not then drive ashore and continue the fight. This was all the Marines wanted to hear, and despite the short time and many other difficulties, they set about modifying their plans. Firstly, of course, the engines had to go back into their tanks, then the men had to be taught to drive, and of course there was the waterproofing to go through. The real problem was back-up. Plans for Overlord were already well advanced and this was no time to make major changes. Consequently no ammunition resupply or maintenance train could be incorporated – the Marines would just have to go ashore and improvise for as long as they could but, to be on the safe side, it was decreed that they should not be allowed to operate more than a mile inland from the beaches.

In practice it proved impossible to get all the tanks to their respective beaches on time. The landing craft had been modified by installing sections of Bailey bridge on the tank deck to ensure that the tanks would be high enough to fire above the level of the vessels' superstructure and ramps. This made the craft top-heavy. Since the weather was far from ideal, most of them found their decks awash during the crossing, and at least one was forced to turn back. Many of those that did arrive landed well behind schedule and in such small numbers that they stood little chance of achieving anything, especially when they found self-propelled artillery already ashore. Thus they received few official calls for help during the first hours and spent their time dealing with targets of opportunity or sorting themselves out. Of the eighty tanks forming the two regiments, only forty-eight came ashore on that first morning. At Langrune-sur-mer in the Oboe sector of Gold Beach, two Centaurs attempted to destroy an anti-tank wall some 6 ft high by 4 ft thick. One ran over a mine and the other used up all its ammunition without seriously disturbing the wall at all, revealing the limitations of the 95-mm howitzer on work that should more properly have been undertaken by a Churchill AVRE. Four more fared much better against the Riva-Bella battery covering the mouth of the Orne, supporting French and British commandos in a successful attack. The many difficulties notwithstanding, the Royal Marine

Armoured Support Group was still fighting fifteen days later, by which time it had progressed up to ten miles inland. Distinguished by bearings painted on their turrets, in ten degree increments for fire control purposes while shipborne, used in conjunction with a special gun-aimer's periscope and plotting board, these were the only Centaur gun tanks to be used on active service by British forces. When the unit was finally withdrawn, on 24 June, their tanks appear to have been handed over to the French Army.

Another unique application of tanks took place on the evening of D-Day, when General Aircraft Hamilcar gliders swept down into fields on the east side of the Orne river and disgorged some Tetrarch light tanks. This event marked the arrival, direct to the battlefield by air from Britain, of light tanks and Universal Carriers of 6th Airborne Reconnaissance Regiment. They had flown, each glider under tow from a Halifax bomber, from Tarrant Rushton airfield in Dorset and their purpose was to provide support for 6th Airborne Division which had been there since early morning. Being so small, the tanks could hardly be considered more than a token gesture if an armoured battle had broken out, but they had an immediate effect out of all proportion to their size. The landing coincided with an attempt by 21st Panzer Division to split the Canadian and British forces with a drive to the sea, but the arrival of some 250 gliders, almost in their rear, caused the Germans to change their minds and fall back on Caen. As each glider bumped to a halt the tank, which had already started its engine, began to move forward in the aircraft. This action tripped a cable which released the nose door lock within the aircraft and caused it to swing open. Yet impressive as it was, the arrival of the glider-borne tanks was less than auspicious. One Hamilcar, skidding across the landing zone, collided with a Tetrarch

that had just emerged from another aircraft, with the result that two tanks were immediately written off. Early reconnaissance sorties accounted for two more, one went up on a mine, another dropped into a ditch, while the remainder mostly snagged themselves on discarded parachute lines. These became so tightly wound around the suspension that they could only be removed after hours of work with a blowlamp. Most of the surviving tanks were later dug in around the landing zone and subsequently handed in when the regiment converted to Cromwells.

The battles which followed the landings have been thoroughly recorded by an army of writers for nearly fifty years, and there is no need to recount them here. Under active service conditions the tanks all appeared to respond well enough, although the difficult countryside did not help. The Bocage, with its high field banks and sunken lanes was a defender's paradise, until Sergeant Curtis G Culin, serving with the 102nd Cavalry Reconnaissance Squadron, United States Army, came up with the answer. A jagged steel blade mounted on the nose of a tank enabled it to slice the top off a field bank and get through without rearing up and exposing its vulnerable underside to enemy weapons. The Americans called this contraption Rhinoceros, while the more prosaic British name was Prong. On D+40 or thereabouts REME was ordered to produce twenty-four samples, which were all ready within three days, made, as were the American examples, from redundant German beach obstacles. Subsequently T C Jones & Company of Shepherds Bush, London made 600, suitable for fitting to the Sherman V, which were delivered in Normandy by the end of August. They were followed by 1,000 Prong II, which would fit either the Sherman or M10, and 500 Prong III designed for the Cromwell. A Ministry of Supply document reported that 21st Army Group considered the Prong to have been very effective,

106   *Churchills of the 75-mm gun Mark VI type, well covered with spare track links, serving with 4th Battalion the Grenadier Guards moving forward with infantry of 1st Battalion the Suffolk Regiment.*

although when one was tested by FVPE in Britain they announced that it conferred no advantage on the tank to which it was fitted. Another paper, circulated early in September, explained that Prongs were not required for Churchills and had a detrimental effect on their performance. Even so, Churchills were seen with them on.

Although the Allies were now firmly, if not exactly safely, ashore in occupied France, they had left a storm behind them in Britain. The dissatisfaction with British tank design and production that had surfaced in the House of Commons that April was still rumbling on, and it reached the ears of the Commander-in-Chief, General Bernard Montgomery, who had replaced Sir Bernard Paget in January 1944. He wrote a letter dated 25 June 1944 which revealed an attitude, at least in public, which was in stark contrast to that of his predecessor:

My dear Secretary of State,

It has come to my notice that reports are circulating about the value of British equipment, tanks, etc., compared to the Germans.

We cannot have anything of that sort at this time. We have got a good lodgement area, we have built up our strength, and tomorrow we leap on the enemy. Anything that undermines confidence and morale must be stamped on ruthlessly. I have issued the enclosed letter. You may like to have the enclosed photograph.

Yours ever,

[Sgd] B.L. Montgomery.

I have been shelled out of the HQ you came to and am now in a more peaceful area!!

Whatever the photograph might have been, the public letter was clear enough, as the following paragraphs show:

In the fighting to date we have defeated the Germans in battle; and we have had no difficulty in dealing with German armour, once we had grasped the problem. In this connection British armour has played a notable part.

We have nothing to fear from the Panther or Tiger tanks; they are unreliable mechanically, and the Panther is very vulnerable from the flanks. Our 17-pdr. gun will go right through them. Provided our tactics are good we can defeat them without difficulty.

Whatever the Commander-in-Chief really thought, the troops, especially those in armoured vehicles, had their own ideas on the subject. Not all the enemy tanks in Normandy were Panthers and Tigers but they could just as easily have been as far as Allied tank crews were concerned. The Tiger in particular was dreaded, for its reputation had gone before it, and a Panzer IV with extra turret armour, when viewed from the front through a misty sighting-telescope, looked sufficiently like a Tiger at

a glance to satisfy most people. Knowing that such a tank was about induced a feeling of nakedness and even a Churchill Mark VII, which had 152 mm of frontal armour, compared with 100 mm on a Tiger, suddenly seemed to provide little more protection than a tinplate toy. Thus it became the fashion to festoon one's tank with all the spare track links that could be scrounged, without a thought for the effect the additional weight might have on it. Officially the practice was frowned upon and a 21st Army Group report stated: 'It is doubtful whether this affords any protection, and there is no firm requirement for it.' The matter was placed in perspective by Colonel Gordon-Hall. He was writing particularly about circumstances in Italy, but they applied equally to North West Europe. He explained that trials had been carried out under test conditions in Britain and that these had proved that track plates added very little protection in relation to the extra weight carried. Their value was certainly much less than an equivalent weight in extra armour. However, he appreciated that nobody had ever been able to convince tank crews of this – many of them argued persuasively that the complex shape of track links had the added virtue of deflecting projectiles, while some would get quite scientific about it and explain exactly how the tracks ought to be placed. One popular theory was that they should never be welded in place but rather suspended from wire so that they would give when struck by a round, reducing its impact. His suggestion was that, rather than ridicule the practice, on account of its wide acceptance in the field, tanks should in future be designed with the spare track stowed on the glacis instead of the trackguards. He went on to say that this craving for added protection was really symptomatic of a lack of confidence which could only be restored by fitting tanks with thicker armour. Repressive instructions, he added, were pointless because no soldier trained to think for himself would take the slightest notice of them. The same was probably true to some extent of Sergeant Culin's Prong. It might not work every time, and might not be needed half the time, but if the crews believed in it they should be humoured, and even encouraged, for their own peace of mind.

Since it was Allied policy that the British and Canadians should transfix the main German forces in Normandy – who in any case were obeying their leader's instruction not to give ground – while the Americans cut a wide swathe around the western and southern flanks, it was inevitable that all the British armour, no matter what its perceived role, would be engaged in this confrontational fighting. Even so there is little doubt that it was the Churchills, in the tank brigades, that bore the brunt of it, at least in the early stages. Most attempts by the armoured divisions to make deep thrusts proved costly against desperate but highly motivated opposition, and it wasn't until the Germans were all but encircled that they gave in and made a break for it. Their last escape route, the Falaise Gap, was closed by 15 August following ten weeks of hard fighting, yet four weeks after that the Allies had swept across France and into Belgium. For the Churchill regiments this marked a period of rest, followed by a systematic reduction of the Channel ports, while the Cromwells, leading the way for a thundering herd of Shermans, had their day. Antwerp was entered on 4 September. In passing, it is worth noting a curious factor recorded at this time. Ammunition expenditure in Normandy had been extremely high, absorbing a large percentage of the available transport. When the breakout began it was appreciated that there would be a massive increase in the demand for fuel and there were fears that sufficient transport might be impossible to find to sustain the advance. In practice it was discovered that in such mobile warfare far less shooting was done, so the demands on ammunition dropped as the need for fuel increased.

Now is a good point to pause and examine how the various British and American armoured vehicles had fared. Reports came in thick and fast, and many of the comments given below are based on those made by the Deputy Director of the Royal Armoured Corps following a visit to 21st Army Group and by General Montgomery.

The Churchill is said to have done extremely well and to have been popular with its crews, while the heavy Churchill, the A22F, was liked for its ability to absorb punishment. The gun had been the problem and crews had been clamouring for a 17-pounder. Close-range fighting was the order of the day in the Bocage, but in any case the 75-mm gun committed the Churchill to close-range action and, as the DDRAC remarked, at such ranges, no armour could stand up to the 88-mm gun, or even the long 75-mm in the Panther. Montgomery felt that the Churchill was underpowered.

The Cromwell seems to have surprised everyone by its reliability, although again its 75-mm gun left a lot to be desired. There was also some feeling in the reconnaissance regiments that it was too thinly armoured underneath. A mine would penetrate the floor plates and kill the crew by blasting them against the roof, so requests were made for this area to be strengthened. In fact when judged as a reconnaissance tank, the Cromwell came to be regarded as less than ideal, despite its remarkable speed and manœuvrability. It was still too large and much too noisy for stealthy reconnaissance and, once the close Normandy countryside had been left behind, the armoured cars returned to popularity. Montgomery still felt that the Cromwell needed too much maintenance attention, but it remained popular with its crews. When 3rd and 4th County of London Yeomanry amalgamated that August, officers from the latter reckoned that the Cromwells they had just given up were in every way superior to the Shermans they would now have to work with. This may have been nothing more than a case of the devil you know, but the sentiment was echoed by Major-General Gerald Verney, commanding 7th Armoured Division. Writing to the DRAC, Raymond Briggs, he praised the Cromwell as 'superb' and claimed that mechanical breakdowns had been so few as to be negligible, even when the tanks had been driving and fighting so continuously that they had hardly received any maintenance at all. He finished off:

> The tremendous speed, when the going has been good, has alone made this great advance possible, and I wish that you and the people who have made the tanks could have seen them tearing along through all these French and Belgian villages. It has been a most inspiring sight and it has thrilled the inhabitants to a really remarkable degree, especially here in Belgium.

One detail seen on these tanks which aroused a lot of interest was the so-called Normandy Cowl. War, it is said, is 10 per cent action and 90 per cent waiting about, and this can give rise to problems which never show up during training. In the case of Cromwell tanks, long periods of standing in line, with the engines on tickover, waiting for the signal to advance, nearly gassed the crews. Fumes from the exhaust hovered around each tank in a choking cloud and were sucked in through the fighting compart-

107 Well-camouflaged Cromwells fighting among the hedgerows.

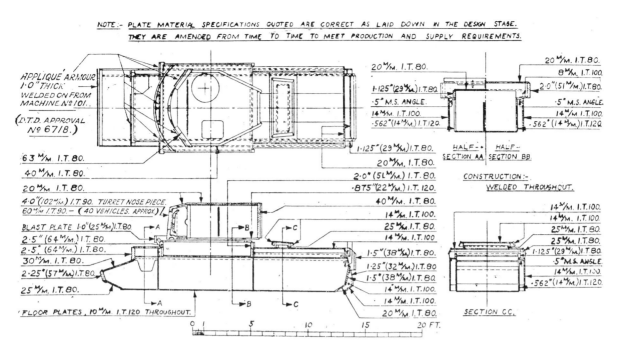

Drawing J: *Armour profile chart of the A30 Challenger showing the extra plates added to the hull and turret front.*

ment, making crews ill and threatening to choke the engine itself. A form of cowl was devised which was mounted over the exhaust outlet in such a way that it diverted the gases downwards and out of harm's way. At first they were knocked up and fitted by each unit's REME detachment, but in due course a standard pattern was devised and supplied in kit form by base workshops.

It is not so easy to find balanced comments on the Challenger. The tank had not taken part in the Normandy landings because no deep-wading gear had been produced for it, and for various reasons they were only slowly coming into service. The 4th County of London Yeomanry took delivery of two just before they amalgamated, and then promptly had to lose them again without taking them into action. The 8th Hussars had some by early September and apparently had no complaints, yet a month later the whole lot were withdrawn to have front idler-wheel problems remedied. When work began on building the second batch of 100, an effort was made to improve armour protection by welding 25-mm cheek pieces to the front of the turret on either side of the mantlet and on all vertical frontal surfaces, while a blast plate had been added to protect the turret ring. Montgomery, writing somewhat earlier, had described Challenger as an improved Cromwell and thought that they should replace Cromwell as soon as sufficient became available, apparently not realising that only 200 were to be built in all. In reply General Weeks told him that it was only an interim design which was not proving entirely satisfactory and that production on a large scale was not justified.

Further comments on reconnaissance were made by the Brigadier, RAC with 34th Tank Brigade. He told DDRAC

108 A 75-mm gun AEC Mark III armoured car leading Staghounds of the 2nd Battalion, the Household Cavalry in Holland.

that a turretless, mine-proof tank was the real answer. He favoured either the American M24 Chaffee or what he described as the Vickers light tank, by which he presumably meant the A25 Harry Hopkins, but he was also very interested in the 95-mm self-propelled version, the Alecto, which was being considered as a replacement for the 75-mm gun half-tracks. At the same time the AEC Mark III armoured car had proved too big and too unwieldy, so the report claimed that it was being withdrawn from armoured car regiments, although some seem to have remained in service. Scout cars, on the other hand, were proving almost too popular. Due to a shortage of turretless Stuart reconnaissance tanks the scout cars were being used instead, never mind what the regimental establishment table said they should be used for. Fighting units were almost universal in expressing a preference for the Daimler over the Humber on account of its thicker armour and multiple reverse speeds but, the report added ruefully, brigade REME officers prefered the Humber because it gave less mechanical trouble. The 4th Armoured Brigade, on the other hand, added that the Humber Scout Car was getting rather a bad name for itself on mines.

The Sherman was not commented upon in any great detail, but it has been saved until last for other reasons. A report from 4th Armoured Brigade was extremely critical of the Whirlwind-engined versions, M4 and M4A1. The engines seem to have required replacement on average every 600 to 700 miles. Brigade workshops had already changed thirty and expected to deal with another 100 in the near future (and remember they were writing a mere twelve weeks after the landing). A further twenty-three tanks had been evacuated with faulty synchromesh in their gearboxes, a failing that brigade workshops remembered from the early Grants. By way of contrast, they regarded the 17-pounder Sherman, the Firefly, as invaluable and called for two per troop as soon as possible. This, however, was just the top layer of a whole can of worms that was about to be opened.

On 6 July 1944 General Montgomery, writing from his tactical headquarters, caused a bulky memorandum to be dropped on to the desk of the Under-Secretary of State for War. A covering letter reminded the Under-Secretary that the writer had been charged by General Eisenhower with the conduct of the battle in France and that, as such, he had a direct interest in both British and American equipment. Anticipating the gist of his memorandum, Montgomery then went on to say that he wished the American troops to have the best available tank gun as soon as possible, and that gun, in Monty's view, was the 17-pounder. His proposal was that once every British

109 A Sherman Firefly of a Canadian regiment in Holland thickly covered with additional track plates.

Sherman regiment had been equipped with Fireflys on the scale of two per troop, deliveries should be diverted to the US Army in Europe until it was able to field one Firefly per platoon. Britain would then add one more per troop to its regiments, then the Americans, and so on. Extracts from the memorandum itself have already been quoted elsewhere. It began by teaching its readers at the War Office to suck eggs, explaining precisely what a tank was, then ran on for just over three pages which distil into a eulogy to the 17-pounder and the usual demand for a universal, or capital tank.

The immediate response from the War Office, written two days later, largely agreed with Montgomery's views but offered few helpful suggestions. After further consideration the situation was explained to the C-in-C in greater detail by Sir Ronald Weeks in letters dated 10 July and 5 August 1944. These explained in the first place that plans had been made to expand Firefly production and that, in theory, what Montgomery chose to do with them in theatre was up to him. The biggest bottleneck was simply the supply of suitable Sherman tanks. Without explaining more fully, it went on to say that only certain marks of Sherman were suitable for conversion and that special conditions also applied to the 105-mm Sherman close support tanks and the new 76-mm gun in the enlarged T23 turret. In the case of the 105-mm it was pointed out that this tank, on account of its role, only had manual turret traverse, which would be quite unsuitable for use with a high-velocity weapon. The T23 turret was another matter entirely.

Although heavily promoted in the United States, the 76-mm gun proved a grave disappointment. Not only was its performance nowhere near as good as the British 17-pounder, it was only marginally better than the old 75-mm weapon and at the same time it was virtually useless firing high explosive – a fact which prompted Montgomery to say that he did not want it for the British Army at all. Since it forms no part of this present study one need not labour the matter, but just to confirm the point, it is worth remarking that documents exist to show that General Eisenhower's reaction to the news that the 76-mm did not compare with the British gun was about as violent as that placid man ever became: 'Why is it that I am always the last to hear about this stuff; Ordnance told me this 76-mm would take care of anything the Germans had. Now I find you can't knock out a damn thing with it.' Weeks explained to Montgomery that for technical reasons it was impossible to install the 17-pounder in the T23 turret without a major redesign programme, and that could only be undertaken at the expense of progress on the new British tank A41, which the War Office was not prepared to contemplate. Indeed he told Monty that the British might have to accept 76-mm gun Shermans in due course, whether he liked it or not. Returning to the 17-pounder, Weeks was prepared to make two proposals: either the Americans sent over their own tanks for the

Royal Ordnance Factory to convert – and the estimated American requirement was for 700 tanks, which ROF could convert at the rate of 100 per month – or the necessary guns and instructions for fitting could be supplied to the Americans. The main drawback here, as Weeks saw it, was that the Americans were unlikely to establish a conversion centre in Britain or liberated Europe, so it would mean shipping everything back to the United States and the delay alone precluded that.

Two events now conspired to render the whole scheme impossible and even, for a while, to throw the whole future of the European Campaign into doubt. The first was purely a British matter involving the port of Antwerp. Although this fell quickly into British hands in quite good condition, it was a long way from the sea, and that route, the Scheldt river and in particular its estuary, was firmly in German hands. Buoyed-up by the success of his charge across Europe, Montgomery elected to push on, leaving the opening of Antwerp until later. Thus his supply of tanks, shipped over from Britain, still relied on the vast Rear Maintenance Area in Normandy. As the supply lines lengthened the Armoured Replacement Groups had their work cut out just bringing the tanks forward. Shipment of tanks through Normandy ceased on 5 September in anticipation of the rapid opening up of Antwerp, but losses were greater than expected so that reserve stocks fell to an all-time low on 27 September. To make matters worse, large numbers of damaged, but repairable, tanks lay scattered along the route from Rouen to Brussels, yet the strain on recovery facilities prevented these from being salvaged at the time when they were most needed. The river route to Antwerp docks was not finally opened until 26 November so, for the previous two months, tanks were being brought in through Ostend and Boulogne at the rate of forty per day. It was a close-run thing for a while, but in due course it proved sufficient not only to replace battle and mechanical wastage but to enable a large reserve stock to be built up rapidly. It would soon be needed.

The second crisis was created by the German counterattack in the Ardennes – the Battle of the Bulge – in December 1944. Losses of Shermans doubled the average monthly figure for the theatre; to place it in perspective, the total figure for US Army Shermans of all types lost between 20 November 1944 and 20 January 1945 was 1,137. And this occured at a critical time. The Americans were already considered to have underestimated their reserve requirements by British standards and, at the same time, they were in the process of changing over to 76-mm gun tanks; production of some 75-mm models had already ceased. To quote official statistics again, the unit entitlements for Shermans calculated in November 1944 were 7,591 American and 7,159 British, yet the respective reserves stood at 3,759 and 6,434. That was a total availability of 10,253 Shermans for the United States Army against 14,273 for the British. There is no doubt where the Americans would come when they needed more.

On 26 December an emergency operational signal was sent from American to British forces requesting the loan of as many Shermans, up to a total of 500, as could be spared. In all 351 were extracted from units, had their wireless layout changed to meet American requirements by REME and had been transported to American vehicles parks by 1 January 1945. What made this feat even more remarkable was the weather. It was so cold that many tanks in reserve parks showed no interest in starting at all, until the Royal Air Force came up with some special engine heaters which solved that problem. There might have been more tanks to spare, but the Ardennes affected British units too. The 29th Armoured Brigade had already been chosen as the first to operate the new A34 Comet tank and had handed its Shermans in when the storm broke. In order to provide an armoured backstop on the Meuse, lest the Germans should have broken through, they were hurriedly restored to their Shermans and did not undergo the changeover until January.

The fact that the Americans knew how many Shermans Britain held was the result of an earlier panic. In August 1944 General Joseph Stilwell, the American *de facto* commander of Chiang Kai-shek's Chinese Army, had requested that 116 Shermans be transferred to him from British stocks in India, on the promise of replacement. Since it was below establishment, although far better off than American units in the theatre, India had refused Stilwell's request. Further pressure was brought to bear, however, and the tanks were reluctantly handed over, never to be replaced. This relatively small incident had rung alarm bells in Washington, especially among those who already felt that the President's Lend-Lease arrangements were too generous. It resulted in what became known as the Global Tank Review, which was conducted by both sides along the lines of a gigantic poker game, with very heavy stakes.

As a first move Britain cabled Washington a list of current holdings of Shermans (for, despite its grandiose title, this review was all about Shermans) without reconciling the figure against previous deliveries. This discrepancy was quickly picked up in Washington and questions were asked. Suspicions were aroused when the Americans concluded that the British were wasting Sherman tanks by converting them to other purposes, notably armoured recovery vehicles, mine flails, observation post and command tanks. Britain pointed out that, apart from the recovery vehicles, which were desperately needed in any case, all the other types retained their 75-mm guns and were still, therefore, justifiable as fighting tanks. There was further embarrassment when it was revealed that the returns for Italy had not included the 17-pounder and 76-mm gun Shermans operating in that theatre, which accounted for about 1,000 tanks. Things got so bad that in December South Africa was asked to release 114 of its Shermans, and even Gibraltar, which only had twelve to start with, had nine of them taken away! There is no doubt that this review, which took nearly four months to complete, revealed something of a shambles in British recording techniques, and this despite the fact that since June 1944 British AFV holdings and losses in the European theatre had been recorded mechanically on mobile Hollerith punched card system equipment supplied by the United States and housed in three big Chevrolet semi-trailer units.

By 1943, as a result of early combat experience, a number of improvements had been developed for the Sherman and incorporated in production. By the end of the year this programme had been extended to earlier tanks, which were returned to Detroit, stripped back to basic components and rebuilt to the new standard. Besides replacing worn-out items, many new features were applied such as additional panels of armour over vulnerable spots, extended-width tracks, gun-support crutches, and in some cases direct-vision cupolas. At first the tanks so treated were training machines no longer required in the United States, but when this work was completed, the US War Department started to look overseas. British commands in all theatres of war were included, and the policy adopted was to recommend for rebuild those tanks otherwise judged to be beyond economical repair at base workshop level. Tanks thus selected then had to be inspected by an American representative before return shipment could be authorised. This caused more problems. Most theatres found it almost impossible to locate a representative with the requisite training and authority, while in Britain it was announced that no tank would be acceptable for rework which was already beyond the state at which it could be repaired locally and that, as far as Britain was concerned, was uneconomical anyway.

The exultation of the drive across Europe had caused some to believe, or at least to hope, that the war could be ended by December 1944. It might be interesting to discover if a war ever did end at Christmas. But the Germans were falling back on the Fatherland and would not abandon their great struggle that easily. They had an ally in the winter weather, which enabled them to flood the lowlands between the Dutch border and the Rhine, and then snow came to make movement even more difficult. The Ardennes and the diversion to link up with the airborne operations on the Rhine occupied the armoured divisions, and the tank brigades were called up to force their way through the deep, dark Reichswald Forest, a task which again proved the need for a well-armoured tank with the mobility to tackle such conditions. It is generally believed that no other Allied tank but the Churchill could have kept going through the deep, clammy mud that soon choked every route. In any case, in such thickly wooded country it was vital for infantry and tanks to work in the closest harness. The tanks were essential to supress strong points, but without the foot soldiers, pacing them in the trees on each side of the track and protecting their flanks, the tanks would have been

110 A Churchill Mark VII experimentally equipped with framed wire mesh screens for added protection against Panzerfaust attack.

vulnerable to German hunting parties with their Panzer-fausts. As already explained, this weapon was also proving troublesome on the Italian Front, where one attempt to defeat it has been described. Photographs of a Churchill, fitted with spaced panels of wire mesh in frames, clearly taken at an establishment in Britain, may record a similar response for Europe, although it could have been intended for use in South East Asia where the Japanese were known to be using hand-placed sticky bombs against tanks. As the battle through this wet and gloomy forest progressed, the resistance offered by the enemy paled into insignificance compared with that effected by nature. Movement along the heavily churned tracks was measured in yards per hour, and tow ropes became more valuable than guns as each tank dragged its neighbour out of the quagmire. If a tank ventured off the track into the woods, then it risked damaging its turret traversing gear when the gun barrel snagged on a tree, just as they did on the vineyard wire in Italy, yet they won through in the end. Now, just ahead, lay Germany's last ditch on the Western Front, the great River Rhine.

Returning now to Normandy and the part played by specialised armour in the D-Day landings, the British and Canadian beaches Gold, Sword and Juno, stretched from Le Hamel in the west to Ouistreham on the Orne estuary in the east. First ashore were the Sherman DD tanks. Of those that landed wet, having swum ashore, losses were surprisingly few, considering the state of the sea. None appear to have attracted attention from the enemy's anti-tank guns, although they were subjected to mortar and small arms fire, one definitely being sunk from a mortar hit. This would appear to confirm that their security was intact up to this time, and that no one guessed they were tanks while they were afloat. With their firepower to back up the first wave of infantry, they proved remarkably successful, although some were swamped. These were the tanks that elected to adopt a hull-down position in the sea but, in the excitement of the moment, forgot to creep forward with the incoming tide. With their aid the Canadians, in particular, were well inland by the first evening.

The Sherman Crabs also proved their worth, getting their flails going as soon as they hit the beach and clearing lanes up to the sea wall ready for the AVREs. They were also much in demand as gun tanks. This was perfectly acceptable in the early stages of the assault, since it was all part of the greater plan, but later they were diverted from their true purpose to provide fire support, and this was not appreciated. Neither was the idea of some local commanders that they should flail all the roads in the area and fields that had been chosen as harbours. This simply wore them out on tasks that could just as easily have been done by troops on foot.

The AVREs proved devastating against concrete emplacements once they had placed, or tried to place their bridges against the sea wall. Again, however, there was a tendency to misuse them as support artillery, at very short range, in the absence of anything better. Bobbins worked well if they were laid on dry beaches but, as already recorded, those laid below the tide line simply got washed away. Bullshorn ploughs were used to turn up mines on beaches where extra craters were unwelcome, and in the dunes above the beaches, but further inland, where the ground got harder, they could not operate. Some AVREs also carried fascines which they used to good effect filling in shell craters and ditches, but as a means of getting a tank up a sea wall they proved useless.

Crocodiles, although not part of 79th Armoured Division at this time, played a very small part on D-Day, only two being reported in action, but their time would come. ARKs are not mentioned at all, either in the Divisional History or the Final Report, so one assumes either that they fulfilled their tasks so well that no remarks were required, or that none were used, which seems unlikely. By contrast, the work of armoured bulldozers, mostly modified Caterpillar D7s, in clearing obstacles under fire is highly praised, causing one to consider how useful some Sherman dozer tanks might have been at this time if any had been available.

The lessons of D-Day, which had been appreciated by the proponents of specialised armour in advance, were quite clear. Such equipment must be husbanded and used with the greatest care in well-planned operations. It should indeed be hoarded, parcelled out only when required and snatched back as soon as the job was done. Otherwise it would inevitably be squandered, misused and ultimately lost. The equipment itself had performed well, although in some cases the requirements were changing.

The ARK is a good example. Its evolution in Britain as a means of climbing sea walls has already been described, but as the 79th Armoured Division moved inland and tackled different obstacles the need changed. Now the ARK was required to fill ditches, and also to carry

111   A Churchill Crocodile of 141st RAC in action near a petrol station in S'Hertogenbosch, Holland in October 1944.

112   A Churchill ARK II, with its longer ramps extended, fills a ditch while photographs are taken for the vehicle handbook.

113 *Ram Kangaroos, transporting infantry, and Universal Carriers, advancing through the winter landscape in Holland.*

wheeled vehicles in addition to tracked. A prototype conversion was done by the Division which involved widening the left-side trackway and then adding longer, 12-ft 6 in. ramps at each end, the left-side ones being wider to match the trackway. Once the design was accepted, fifty sets of equipment to convert all the existing ARKs to the new Mark II standard were made by a firm in Bolton and fitted by REME. It is interesting to note that such was the demand for these ARKs in Europe that it was December 1944 before one could be spared for evaluation by the Fighting Vehicle Proving Establishment in Britain. A request for an ARK with 20-ft ramps was made later, but the strain on the test vehicle was such that they twisted out of shape and the project was abandoned.

It was the Canadians again who initiated the Kangaroo in North West Europe. In August 1944, when their artillery regiments were issued with Sexton self-propelled guns to replace their M7 Priests, they altered the latter into personnel carriers. The conversion was similar, although somewhat superior, to the project carried out in Italy, with the 105-mm howitzer and ammunition stowage removed, the gun aperture plated over and additional armoured panels added on the sides. They were first used during Operation Totalise, south of Caen. During the dash for Antwerp there had been no need for such equipment, but as winter came on, and the Reichswald Forest loomed, the idea was revived.

Now it was decided to use Canadian Ram tanks with their turrets removed; they were called sawn-off Rams. Two regiments, one British, one Canadian, had been incorporated into 79th Armoured Division by December 1944 and they proved most effective. There was still a problem for the passengers, who had to clamber over the sides, but at least these modified tanks had a hull machine-gun which provided some fire support. Each Kangaroo carried eight fully equipped soldiers, and the regimental establishment was geared to infantry arrangements. Thus a section of three Kangaroos could carry one infantry platoon, a troop could manage a company and a squadron could lift an infantry battalion headquarters plus four rifle

companies. As already mentioned, they proved invaluable during the fighting in the Rhineland; they could cover country passable to a Sherman, although it is pointed out in one report that they could not always be expected to follow Churchills wherever those tanks could go. Plans were drawn up to create Centaur Kangaroos, which might have had a height advantage, but there was also a curious scheme devised by REME in Europe to use gutted, turretless cruiser tanks as personnel-carrying trailers. At the end of the war a Churchill Kangaroo appeared.

The United States Army is believed to have used some LVT amphibians during the Normandy Landings, but only in the ship-to-shore supply role. The British first used them during operations in the Scheldt estuary late in October, but here they functioned as assault vehicles, ferrying commandos from landing craft right into action. As on D-Day, 79th Armoured Division created breaching teams of specialised AFVs to suit the situation, and most types were employed except Crocodiles and ARKs. But the low-lying island of Walcheren was almost awash where they landed, and many vehicles were swamped by the sea or bogged down in the mud – all, that is, except the LVTs which the British had nicknamed Buffaloes, and their miniature counterparts, Weasels. The Final Report of the division is very complimentary about both amphibians, claiming that they could outperform any tracked vehicle on flooded or waterlogged country. Even so, the practice of using LVTs to resupply the men they had delivered into action was criticised since by the end of the operation none of the surviving Buffaloes was fit for anything more without a major overhaul. Buffaloes, it said, should only have been used for assault operations, resupply being left to Terrapins, Weasels and DUKWs. Most of the LVTs mounted a pair of .50 calibre Brownings, while many were modified to mount a 20-mm Polsten cannon at the front, but it proved very difficult for the crews to fire any of these weapons without placing themselves in danger.

From the point of view of 79th Armoured Division, the River Rhine posed as many problems as the original landing in Normandy, although they were not all of the same nature. It helped to have had eight months of combat experience to draw upon but, to make doubly sure, the Division opened a number of experimental establishments, or Wings, in Britain and Holland where new techniques could be developed. Two major problems were foreseen for the amphibians: crossing the wide waterway with accuracy, and climbing out on the far side. Pinpoint accuracy was essential in order that established bridgeheads could be reinforced in conditions of poor visibility and a fast-running current. The riverbank presented problems that did not exist on an open beach, being steep in places and very muddy. Buffaloes might be able to cope with it, but Sherman DDs would inevitably get bogged down unless some means was developed helping them. A third problem which was getting serious was that very unpleasant anti-personnel weapon, the S-mine.

Three navigational aids were developed: a gyro direction indicator, radio direction equipment using a ground aerial system, and Tabby. This last, which was still regarded as Top Secret at the end of the war, was a relatively simple infra-red station-keeping system which caused the headlights of one Buffalo to pick up reflectors on the craft in front without showing a beam in total darkness, the image being visible only to those provided with special binoculars. Incidentally, one reason why the Germans refrained from employing their own infra-red equipment in the West was a well-founded belief that Britain was sufficiently advanced in IR technology to have detected it. Another, more obvious, navigational aid used on the Rhine at night was Movement Light. This was the codename for a squadron of CDL tanks stationed on the nearside bank, where their lights provided visibility for the Buffaloes and watched the river to deter sabotage.

Another Wing experimented with forms of carpet which could be carried and laid by a Buffalo to enable DD tanks to gain a purchase on the opposite bank, but the main work on this was done in Britain. At Burton-upon-Stather, on the equally muddy estuary of the River Trent, a whole range of devices were developed to help DD tanks escape from quaggy rivers. They ranged from the prosaic Moses, which was a sort of boat-shaped mat which was floated into position and unfolded, to the spectacular Rocket Egress, in which a battery of aircraft booster rockets was mounted on each side of a DD and fired at the crucial moment. A carpet attachment was also tried; Holy Roller was a lightweight version of Bobbin, mounted on the front of a Valentine DD, while Gin-and-It was a more complex device, as one might expect of anything devised by Nicholas Straussler. It consisted of a large mat, folded in segments and attached to the bow of a Sherman DD, which extended itself as the tank came ashore. Finally there was Hopper, which can best be described as a Sherman DD ARK.

114 Tugboat, the double-tracked version of T16 Carrier for crossing minefields.

The problem presented by the S-mine was different. Things had come a long way since the time in Tunisia when, faced with a field of anti-personnel mines, an entire infantry battalion formed up in line abreast and ran across without a single casualty. Now the Germans were sowing them in ground so soft that a flail tank could not operate over it. F Wing at Gheel, in Belgium, developed roller and plough attachments for the Weasel, while in Britain a T16 Carrier, codenamed Tugboat, fitted with a double set of tracks on each side to reduce ground pressure, was used to tow a Centipede roller. This did not work, but the vehicle was later handed over to the Mud Crossing Committee for mobility trials. Other unsuccessful attempts to explode mines included trying to cook them off with a Crocodile flamethrower – which did not work – and a development of the deadly Conger, known as Tapeworm. This was a two-wheeled trailer, towed by a tank, which contained 1,000 ft of ordinary fire hose, joined up in 50-ft lengths. Before the operation the hose was laboriously filled with cartridges of explosive and flaked down inside the trailer. The towing tank was fitted with CIRD, and the idea was that on reaching the minefield the tank deposited the trailer but carried on across the danger zone, pulling out the hose as it went. Assuming the tank got through unscathed, it pulled the hose clear out of the trailer, at which point it was automatically ignited, causing it to explode and clear a lane 16-ft wide of 95 per cent of the Teller mines in its path. The drawback, inevitably, was the CIRD, which could not be relied upon to work consistently over such distances.

If any proof is needed for the success of specialised armour, especially in the last year of the War, then it can be found by studying the growing number of items entering service or under development by the time the Germans surrendered. Surely such an orgy of invention would never have been sanctioned if there had been any doubt as to its value? Maybe it was too much. The idea might have got abroad that machines could be designed to do everything, and that is a dangerous course to pursue. From December 1944 until the war ended, and for at least two years afterwards, the amount of experimentation was prodigious and no attempt can be made to chronicle the entire subject here. However, some of these devices are too important or spectacular to ignore, and at least two were issued to service units.

The most important was the Centaur Dozer. Although some British units were equipped with the eminently successful Sherman Dozer, a British type was considered essential and it was developed in prototype form by the 79th Armoured Division in Belgium. Production was then undertaken by the MG Car Company at Abingdon. It consisted of a Centaur cruiser tank, stripped of its turret and fitted with a full-width bulldozer blade which pivoted on a skeleton framework outside the road wheels. A turret, preferably armed with a 95-mm howitzer, might appear to have been a logical feature of such a tank, but this could

115 *A Centaur Dozer, with its blade raised, which appears to have damaged a house.*

not have been mounted because the blade was controlled by cables and the winch was installed in the fighting compartment. Why a hydraulic system could not have been employed – as was the case with a version fitted to a Crusader gun tractor – is not clear, although it might have had something to do with the Travelling Hoist device which the British insisted on adding to the hydraulic Sherman Dozer. The Centaur's turret ring was plated over, and an armoured conning tower added at the front for the commander, but only a few had been issued by the time the war in Europe ended.

Ever since the original Petard had been developed by Colonel Blacker there had been a demand for something more powerful, especially something with a greater range. Either that, or users wanted more armour on the grounds that highly trained AVRE crews were more precious than most and should not be obliged to work at ranges where they were suicidally vulnerable to the larger German weapons. This proving impossible, a scheme was devised for a better weapon. At first this caused a curious demarcation dispute since, it was argued, anything fired at above point blank range demanded gunnery skills which, for some reason, sappers were not deemed capable of assimilating. Already the Canadian pioneer, Captain Denovan, had created a simpler form of Petard which he christened Buffalo, but since this could not achieve a greater range than the existing type it was abandoned in favour of a 9.5-in. weapon called the Ardeer Projector, or Ardeer Aggie, which had an effective range of 450 yards. It was based on the work of Sir Dennistoun Burney of Ardeer on the Strathclyde coast. Burney was a pioneer of recoilless weapons, which he made a range of throughout the war, none of which was ever adopted for service. In order to counter the effect of recoil, such a gun has either to discharge projectiles of equal weight in opposite directions, or to expel a high-velocity jet of flaming gas through a series of blast pipes in opposition to the shell. This last being considered particularly lethal in a tank, the former process was chosen and the weapon installed in a Churchill Mark III. The gun tube ran clear through the

turret from front to back but, since it could not be loaded from outside it was designed to slide open in the middle to receive the 54-pound HE round and a counter projectile, weighing 48 pounds that was filled with sand.

The equipment was tested by the Assault Training and Development Centre at Woodbridge in Suffolk. It resulted in a host of problems. Vulnerability was one. Openings in both faces of the turret reduced its structural rigidity and, even with its limited elevation – which also inhibited the choice of targets – large gaps appeared around the weapon, especially at the back of the turret. Then there were stowage and loading difficulties. For every projectile carried there had to be a counter projectile, and loading both every time was tiring work. Finally, although it was better than a great gout of flame, a 48-pound bag of sand bursting all over the tank's engine deck was not exactly welcome. To cap it all, the weapon proved inaccurate above 300 yards and nothing like as effective against concrete as the ordinary Petard, so the project was dropped.

For sheer spectacle, nothing could compare with Great Eastern. It was another brainchild of Colonel Jefferis' organisation MD1 and the first prototype was built on a turretless Churchill I hull. The object was a form of ARK which could throw its ramp up and over a high wall. The ramp came in three sections. The centre one, resting above the hull of the tank, was at a fixed angle. The short rear one, by means of which other tanks mounted, was slung at the rear, while the front ramp, which was equal in length to the centre one, lay folded back upon it. The tank approached an obstacle, the driver judging his distance by means of a retractable measuring device, and at the appropriate moment let the rear ramp fall and activated the front one. This was literally launched by rockets which lifted the rear end, causing it to swing in an arc around the hinges that joined it to the centre ramp, until it fell across the obstacle. The whole launching process was said to take 2½ seconds. Ten prototypes were built on Churchill IV hulls which had heavy Churchill Mark VII suspension and tracks, and following trials which proved that the idea worked they were issued to 21st Army Group in Europe. One was fired off to celebrate the German surrender, at Deventer in Holland, but they never saw operational use.

Despite the fact that they always seemed to be a rather imprecise instrument, rockets appear to have been favoured by devisers of specialised armour. In addition to the prodigious Great Eastern, three other designs of ARK were contemplated which launched their ramps this way. All three were based on Churchill and two – Foldupus, which emanated from Italy and Woodlark, its British counterpart – were built as prototypes. Hudnott ARK, the third design, never progressed beyond the scale-model stage. Rockets in a more directly offensive role were a feature of Woodpecker, which was based on the Churchill AVRE. Batteries of four were mounted on each side of the turret, the projectiles being fitted with Petard explosive

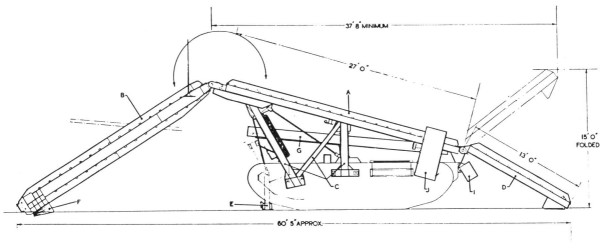

A — FIXED RAMP   F — SHOCK ABSORBER
B — PROJECTED RAMP   G — DISTANCE MEASURING DEVICE
C — SUPPORTS   H — ELECTRICAL SYSTEM (EXTERNAL)
D — REAR RAMP   I — ROCKET MAGAZINE
E — FRONT SPRAG   J — ROCKET DISCHARGE BOX

Drawing K: *Great Eastern, showing how the ramps unfold.*

116 Great Eastern, being used by a Churchill gun tank to cross a wall during a display at Deventer, Holland, on VE Day.

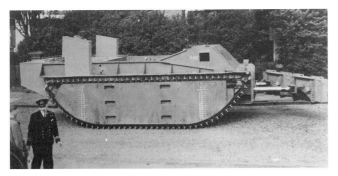

117 Rascal, the remote-controlled LVT I Alligator, showing the hydraulic charge-placer at the front.

heads. The idea was to batter the offending target, sea wall or pillbox, with Petards in rapid succession, rather than suffer the time-consuming business of having one AVRE fire a succession of rounds at it in the usual way. It seems to have worked reasonably well at typical Petard range and might have been adopted, but the risk of having so much explosive material close to the turret on the outside of a tank was considered too great under active service conditions.

One aspect of specialised armour which limits on space preclude us from examining is remote control. Tanks had been tested for this purpose in 1942 but most of the vehicles developed were midgets, not unlike the German Goliath which proved a singular disaster. However, it would be wrong to ignore the impressive Rascal. This was a remote control version of the full-size LVT which carried Bangalore torpedo launchers and a large explosive charge on hydraulic rams at the front. Tested by the Combined Operations Experimental Establishment (COXE) in North Devon its intended role was to swim ashore under radio control, drive up to the selected obstacle and blow it apart.

Since the means by which an atom bomb was being built to deliver the *coup de grâce* to Japan were unknown to most planners in the lower echelons, schemes to assist in the defeat by conventional means continued to develop. One such involved the erstwhile Royal Marine Armoured Support Group which, since its adventures in Normandy, had been reconstituted as 29th Infantry Battalion, Royal Marines. Some of its members had clearly enjoyed their stint in armour and, when Britain took delivery of some new American amphibians in February 1945, the same men formed 34th Amphibian Support Regiment, Royal Marines, to operate them. The new equipment was the

LVT(A)4 which in effect was the rear-engined LVT 2 with a 75-mm howitzer mounted in an open-topped turret. Supplemented with technical personnel drawn from the Army, the regiment went out to India to collect its equipment and train in the amphibious assault role. Two of its four batteries used the LVT(A)4, making twenty-four vehicles in all. These could fire while swimming ashore, from a range of 500 yards, with far more effect than the old Centaurs would have done strapped down in their landing craft. When the attackers hit the beach the LVTs would remain hull down in the water giving fire support and, as the fighting moved inland, keeping pace with it, still firing. The two other batteries were equipped with conventional LVT 4 Buffaloes modified to other roles. One, the flame battery, was equipped with ten Sea Serpents. These were Buffaloes mounting a pair of Wasp flame projectors on prefabricated stands, along with fuel and propellant tanks in the hold. Trials in Britain revealed that in anything but a calm sea, spray would extinguish the igniters, but in good conditions they worked well enough. Finally there was the rocket battery, which had a dozen Buffaloes. These had a tray of Hedgehog launchers in the cargo hold which could launch seventy-two projectiles in three minutes. The war ended suddenly, however, before they could be employed as intended, and they returned to Britain in 1946 where they served as a demonstration regiment until disbandment in 1948.

118 An LVT (A) 4, with its open-topped 75-mm howitzer turret, as used by 34th Amphibian Support Regiment RM.

119 Sea Serpent, the LVT IV Buffalo with two Wasp flamethrowers and a machine-gun turret, developed by 79th Armoured Division.

8 Final analysis

In February 1945 Field Marshal Montgomery, as he had now become, felt it incumbent upon himself to deliver another morale-boosting eulogy on tanks. This one, oft-quoted, was to go down in history. It was to the effect that if von Runstedt had been equipped with British cruiser tanks, instead of Tigers and Panthers, his strike out of the Ardennes would have crossed the Meuse and probably reached Antwerp. By the same token, Monty declared, if his own regiments had been equipped with Tigers and Panthers, instead of British cruisers, they would never have achieved the advance from Normandy to Holland in six days. It is to be hoped that when he spoke of British cruisers Montgomery did not intend to exclude the mass of Shermans that backed them up.

The facts support the Field Marshal in as much as von Runstedt never did get across the Meuse, and British cruisers did achieve that dash across Europe, but to what extent they were accepted by the men in the tanks is less certain. Anyone trying to face down a Panther with a Sherman Firefly, only to see the 17-pounder rounds glancing off the sloping glacis plate, and knowing that any second the reply would smash clear through his own tank, could be excused for taking a different line. And anyone hoping to persuade the crew of a Panther which had just survived that experience to trade it for a Cromwell might expect to have his work cut out. Yet Raymond Briggs, the Director, Royal Armoured Corps, seized upon it. Writing to the DCIGS on 17 February 1945, concerning the awkward subject of Parliamentary Questions on Tanks, he welcomed Montgomery's tribute. He acknowledged that some questions asked in the House proved to be a 'slight embarrassment' to the government, but his real concern was that they undermined the confidence of tank crews and factory workers. He did not know whether to attribute them to concern or malice. If the latter, then he knew that nothing could be done to counter such comments, but if it was well-meant ignorance he could remedy it, and enclosed a summary of the present situation which was prepared to do just that.

Briggs's paper was, technically, correct. It compared the theoretical performance of the 17-pounder against the 75-mm gun in the Panther, the 88-mm in the Tiger, and the new 88-mm in the Royal Tiger and it proved, on paper, that firing the new armour-piercing discarding sabot (APDS) round, the 17-pounder outperformed all of them. It confirmed the view that all these heavy German tanks were formidable defensive armoured machines, but explained that in the open they were often vulnerable. All

of which was quite true – in theory. His final conclusion, however, smacked more of the sentiment that Monty knew best: 'I am satisfied that we are better guided by compliance with the requirements of our Commanders-in-Chief in the field than by the more frequent reiterations of persons less qualified to dictate policy on military weapons.' The DCIGS was pleased, and forwarded the paper to the office of the Secretary of State for War with the endorsement 'It is short and good and might be welded into his estimate speech.' It was, and the press pounced on Montgomery's phrase for the benefit of a wider audience.

In seeking for a voice from the turret to counter Monty's claim, one does not have to look far: 'Supposing I were challenged to a duel by a German tank commander and the choice of weapons lay between the Mark IV Panzer, as used in the first years of the war, and a British Cromwell as used for the first time in June, 1944, I would choose the German Mark IV.' The writer was Major R J Crisp MC, a famous South African Test cricketer of pre-war days. The sentence is taken from a letter, dated 11 March 1945, which he wrote to the crusading MP Richard Stokes. One can pick up on some of Crisp's statements just as one can Mongomery's. If the Panzer IV was a really early one, with the short 75-mm gun, would he still have been so keen? And if the duel involved manoeuvre as well as firepower, might not the Cromwell have run rings around his opponent? What one cannot argue with is the basic sentiment, especially coming from such an experienced officer. He began his tank career in an A10 Cruiser in Greece and claimed to have fought in seven distinct types of British and American tanks, culminating in the Cromwell. He had had seventeen tanks shot from under him and been wounded four times, so his thoughts deserve to be taken seriously. It was obviously bad enough being expected to fight and win in second-rate tanks, but the worst aspect, from Crisp's point of view, was the unqualified adulation – ballyhoo, Crisp called it – which poured forth from senior Allied officers and politicians in the name of morale. He asked Stokes to imagine what thoughts went through the heads of every tank crew who read this stuff. His most telling paragraph is worth quoting:

> For four years now I have been watching shells fired from mine and other tanks bouncing off the front armour of German Panzers. I mean actually watching and actually bouncing, and that after we have wriggled and crept and rushed our tanks to within effective range for our weapons. This has meant always that for at least 1,000 yards we have been within the enemy's effective range before we could fire a shot that had any hope of success.

Crisp included the 17-pounder in this criticism, having tried one against an abandoned Panther, finding that it took three rounds to effect a penetration of the front plate. He also railed against the 'fast, lightly armoured and therefore more mobile' theory, pointing out that the Russian tanks advancing on Berlin from the east were probably as heavy, if not heavier than Panther or Tiger. Stokes pounced on the letter, which Crisp certainly expected him to make public, and used it as the centrepiece of his own vitriolic attack on the whole system of Allied tank production, and the Prime Minister in particular. Under the title *Some Amazing "Tank" Facts* it was published after the war, and offered for sale at one shilling. Of course, being a politician Stokes could not help overstating his case, and gave the white elephantine TOG tank one last, undeserved plug. Whether it did more than get the thing off his chest is another matter. A war-weary public, grateful only that it was over and that 'we' had won, would be in no mood to be hectored on past mistakes and they especially did not want to hear that thousands of their boys had died through the neglect and politically expedient optimism of those in charge at home. If the document ever did serve a useful purpose, it was an odd one which Stokes could hardly have intended. Precisely forty-seven copies were obtained by the School of Tank Technology after the war and made available, without qualification or comment, to students for study purposes only and 'NOT for general distribution'.

In Chapter 3 brief reference was made to a new, high-velocity 75-mm gun developed by Vickers-Armstrong for which, as it turned out, a new tank would be required. Action was taken at once on a new design to the General Staff specification A34 which, for obvious reasons, would have to be based firmly on Cromwell technology. Leyland Motors were appointed design parents and given the draft specifications, whereupon the Tank Board, at a meeting on 20 July 1943, threw a spanner in the works. Ignoring the fact that the tank had been designed specifically to carry the new Vickers gun, they started to debate whether it might not take the American 76-mm instead. Their argument centred upon the advantage of ammunition compatibility on the grounds that, in due course, Britain should also be operating large numbers of 76-mm gun Shermans. This caused somebody else to suggest that, since it was an even better weapon, the British 17-pounder might be a more sensible choice. This last was rejected on the grounds that the turret was too small, and the Ministry of Supply came down in favour of the 75-mm for production reasons, which meant that the turret would have to be redesigned if it was decided to use the American gun.

Once the design was finalised an order was placed with Leylands for 500, but they were not happy either. They pointed out that in their view the design was simply not progressive enough to warrant introduction throughout their group, and favpired concentrating on the altogether more advanced A41 design instead. Further, they felt that the tank was rendered unnecessary by the Sherman Firefly. The project went ahead all the same. In October 1943 it was announced that the gun was to be modified so that it could fire the 17-pounder APCBC and HE ammunition, and a month later the Tank Board announced that in future it would be known as the 77-mm gun, in order to distinguish it from any other. Shortly afterwards it was declared that the tank filled the specification for a cruiser and that it was to have priority over the A27 Cromwell, but not the A30 Challenger. Detail matters remained to be settled. One required the fitting of the new all-round vision cupola while another, which scarcely seems credible so late in 1943, requested a towing hook for the 17-pounder anti-tank gun rather than the troublesome Rotatrailer. Is it possible to believe that anyone was still seriously considering that descredited piece of equipment, following reports, recounted in the previous volume,[*] concerning the Rotatrailer's poor performance?

It was still hoped to have a few A34s ready by the second quarter of 1944 and the Tank Board announced that they required 500 by late in that same year. Somewhere around this time the total on order seems to have been increased to 2,000, but in fact the mild-steel prototype was not seen until March 1944, and there was still a long way to go. In May it was announced that there was no requirement for a 95-mm version, but in September there was a major disruption of the programme. It was stated that changes would be required to the hull, which was to be entirely of welded construction, and the turret, which would be a composite cast and welded structure. It seems almost unbelievable, after all that had gone before, that any other method of construction would be considered for the hull at such a late date, until it is realised that similar changes had been ordered for the Cromwell not long before. This naturally slowed things down, especially with the turret which raised new problems of its own, although it was still hoped to have 150 ready by December. In fact the figure was 143, and the month January 1945. At this point it was forecast that all 2,000 would be ready by the end of 1945 but, within the month it was agreed to cut back production.

The new tank was named Comet. At a glance it did not look that much different from the Cromwell; yet for all Leyland's reservations, it was a much better tank all round. Mechnically it was identical, with the Meteor engine and Merritt-Brown transmission, although the Christie suspension was employed with track-return rollers on production tanks. This certainly limited deflection on individual wheel stations, but it prevented the top run of the track from slapping against the underside of the trackguards and does not appear to have spoiled the ride unduly. Armour thickness was a maximum of 101 mm at the front, the same as a welded Cromwell, and once again

*D J Fletcher, *The Great Tank Scandal*, HMSO, 1989, p 117.

120   *The Commanding Officer's A34 Comet of 1st RTR passes Field Marshal Montgomery on the saluting base during a parade in Berlin, in September 1945.*

it was stepped to give a vertical face for the driver's visor and hull machine-gun mount. The turret was undoubtedly the most progressive feature of the tank. The main shell was of flat, welded plate of a single thickness, compared with the composite form of the Cromwell, but the front was a casting. This was slightly recessed above turret ring level so that the lower edge of the mantlet was better protected, and to compensate for this there was a considerable overhang at the back to accommodate the wireless set. Comet was heavier than the Cromwell, at 32.5 tons, and slower at 29 mph, but the 77-mm gun had a far better performance than the 75-mm. Firing APDS at a muzzle velocity of 3,675 fps it was only moderately inferior to the 17-pounder; the real difference, however, lay in the fact that it was a complete design in its own right, not an emergency modification like Challenger or the Sherman Firefly. As already recorded it first entered service with the 29th Armoured Brigade, but it did not see action until after the Rhine crossing. Like the Challenger it experienced some problems with the front idler, but despite a short combat career with the British Army, it was soon judged a great success. Needless to say, once the war was over, Leyland Motors made much of this in an account of their war record, but it was well deserved. Despite many irritating changes to the specification they were only six weeks behind the final agreed delivery schedule, and they achieved this without any disruption to Cromwell production at all. It is also worth remarking that the tank passed smoothly from prototype stage into production and then into action, without that trying period of unreliability that had characterised most of its predecessors. Undoubtedly

Robotham of Rolls-Royce was right when he said in his autobiography, referred to earlier, that Comet's potential problems had been ironed out in the Cromwell, although at the end of his book he could not avoid one last dig in favour of his own brainchild, Challenger, saying that it was a case of the bird in the hand being worth two in the bush. With hindsight it seems justifiable, in this case, to query the old saw. If A34 had been given priority over A30 in November 1944, instead of the other way round, it is reasonable to assume that it would have proved far more effective; but that is pointless speculation.

If necessity is the mother of invention, might not desperation, at least, be the father of ingenuity? To come to the point, if the gun on one's tank is not achieving the desired result, might it not be a good idea to cast about for something else? This, at any rate, seems to have occurred to the 1st Battalion, the Coldstream Guards shortly before the Rhine crossing when they got hold of a small quantity of aircraft rockets. These fearsome, unguided missiles were normally carried beneath the wings of Typhoon fighter aircraft and released against ground targets with devastating effect, if they hit. The Coldstreams could not see why the same result might not be achieved by firing them for their Sherman tanks and, assisted by their battalion fitters, had the first set of launching rails rigged up on a tank's turret within twenty-four hours. The rails were mounted, one each side of the turret, roughly aligned with the tank commander's vane sight. The rockets, which were underslung from the rails, were equivalent in size to a 75-mm shell with a 60-pound high-explosive warhead. The main problem to be overcome was aiming them at

121 *Typhoon rockets fitted to the turret of a Sherman of the Coldstream Guards.*

anything. A rocket-firing Typhoon, diving on its target, was normally travelling at ground 400 mph and in theory the rocket, once launched, would hold on to this course while the aircraft pulled away. By contrast a Sherman tank could only launch its rocket at 0 mph; it had to be stationary. The result was that the rocket would first dip as it detached from the launching rail, and then gain speed along its chosen course, more or less. By trial and error the Guards discovered that the rocket had a maximum range of about 800 yards, but it would hit anything standing in its way at 400 yards and when it did, the morale effect was described as tremendous. On one occasion a bridge was captured when the first rocket destroyed an 88-mm gun that was covering it, while on another the enemy were driven out of a wood they had been defending after two rockets were fired through it. Road blocks were the Guards' favourite target – the rockets simply blew them away, but they never had the opportunity to try them against an enemy tank. All the same, they were quite confident that if they ever had hit one, the turret was likely to have been blown clean off.

Among the reports filtering back to Britain from the front line, even those which might now be considered unduly biased in a favourable way to British tank design, there was general agreement that the Churchill was under-gunned. It was not suggested that all these tanks needed a larger weapon, but that within each squadron, even each troop, something mounting a 17-pounder would be a great help for dealing with enemy armour. This was quite impossible as things stood, because the diameter of the Churchill's turret ring precluded it, but the matter had been considered. In May 1943 Lieutenant-Colonel F D W O'Rorke, the experimental officer at Lulworth, wrote to the School of Tank Technology suggesting an improved Churchill. He began by proposing the new Vickers high-velocity 75-mm gun, but favoured something bigger if the turret ring diameter could be enlarged. He wanted the armour to be increased by 1 in. and suggested that weight

could be saved by adopting a single-skin welded hull. Lowering the height of both sprockets and idler wheels, he thought, would give a better ride and among his other suggestions were a Cromwell-type front hull machine-gun mounting, all-round vision cupola, and dual controls for the co-driver. Finally he requested that this, and all future tank designs, should be simplified by reducing the number of types and sizes of nuts and bolts.

Nothing was done specifically to implement Colonel O'Rorke's suggestions, although thoughts about an improved Churchill were in the air. Draft specifications were issued on 2 December 1943 for what amounted to an improved Churchill with the General Staff specification A43. It was to mount a 17-pounder, or possibly a 3.7-in. gun, and the Department of Tank Design suggested that it might feature sloped armour. The estimated weight was 50 tons. On 28 December 1943 Vauxhall Motors took a Churchill tank, which they described as having a 'special five-speed gearbox', and loaded it up to 50 tons to see that would happen. In a comparative trial against an A33 Assault Tank, weighted to the same figure, the Churchill was described as 'hardly worse', which could be taken any number of ways, although it would not mean much in any of them. This caused one commentator to point out that A43 was inevitably going to be underpowered, especially when compared with the Panther or the Tiger, and he wished it to be remembered that the latter was well over two years old at that time. He suggested a 600-hp Meteor engine for the new tank instead of the 350-hp Bedford that Vauxhalls were intending to use. Meanwhile the Department of Tank Design put forward a scheme for fitting the new A41 turret.

In May 1944 it was agreed to order six prototypes, giving priority to a version mounting the 17-pounder with an independent 20-mm cannon fitted alongside it. Next in line was to be a 77-mm gun version, and finally a 95-mm howitzer armed close support model. This was to be followed by an order for 300 of the 17-pounder type with delivery planned to begin around May or June 1945, which would then be succeeded by a Meteor-engined version. DRAC was reluctant to support the project, on the grounds that the tank would be underpowered. It is noteworthy that as it got closer to production, and this point was raised on subsequent occasions, the official line was that it was now too late to change; the implication being that this was a new idea, dreamed up at the last minute and liable to upset production! A full-size wooden mock-up was inspected at Vauxhall's Luton factory on 29 August 1944 and the first prototype was completed on 6 January 1945. Now known as Black Prince, its parentage was obvious in the shape of the hull and running gear, which was clearly Churchill on the grand scale. Strangely, in the case of any new British tank, it tipped the scales at close to its estimated weight, and one could see how the suspension had been beefed up to cope with it. For all that, frontal armour, at 152 mm, was no thicker than on a

122 *A43, Black Prince, photographed at Lulworth. The similarity with Churchill is obvious, but the air-intakes have been moved from the sides to the engine deck.*

late-model Churchill, while the speed was no better than 11 mph. The turret was also Churchill-style although the mantlet arrangement was similar to that of the contemporary Comet. Contrary to original suggestions the 17-pounder gun shared its coaxial mounting with a standard Besa, rather than the proposed 20-mm weapon, and there was another Besa in the stepped hull front.

Prototype number 3 was examined at Lulworth and the preliminary report, published in March 1945, expressed disappointment at the flat hull front. It also disapproved of what it described as the 'intricate mantlet' which, it suggested, invited trouble under armour piercing attack. On the positive side the armament was found to be well-balanced and the turret traverse good, but it was not Lulworth's place to comment on performance. The war ended before production got under way and six prototypes only were constructed. One report implies that one of them was fitted with a Meteor engine, but this has never been confirmed so no performance figures are available. Black Prince, like Tortoise, did not fit in with post-war concepts on tank design or standardisation so it had no future and just one of the prototypes was retained as a sample of a tank which, in everything but performance, could most safely be described as the British Tiger.

Operation Veritable, the clearing of the Reichswald Forest – which incorporated part of the Siegfried Line – was completed in early March 1945 and the Allied armies now faced up to their biggest challenge since crossing the Channel: the River Rhine. As with that earlier operation, crossing this waterway was largely a task for specialised armour, although some M22 Locust light tanks were landed by Hamilcar gliders in support of 6th Airborne

Division. The final two months of the war in Europe were like nothing that had gone before. In terms of tanks, at least in the west, Germany had shot its bolt with the Ardennes counterattack and was now reduced to scraping them up from training schools and experimental establishments. For its last, desperate defence the Wehrmacht relied heavily on self-propelled anti-tank guns in ambush positions and infantry tank-hunters with hand-held, but none the less destructive, hollow-charge weapons.

It is hardly surprising if, at this late stage, with the war as good as won, the Allies displayed more caution than do or die. From the armour point of view this was reflected in a massive increase in expenditure of small arms (machine-gun) ammunition in relation to main armament; a statistic that prompted some foolish people to voice some very unwise conclusions after the war. These conclusions were drawn partly from first-hand experience, but largely from a remarkable publication produced under the auspices of the Medical Research Council in January 1946.

Entitled *A Survey of Casualties Amongst Armoured Units in North West Europe* it was compiled by two Royal Army Medical Corps Captains, Harkness and Wright. In the main it concerned itself with British armoured regiments in Sherman, Stuart, Cromwell and Challenger tanks, although reference was made to Churchill casualties and those suffered by the Canadians. It covered the period 24 March to 5 May 1945, that is from immediately after the Rhine crossing to the end of the war, and it surveyed 333 damaged tanks and 769 damaged human beings. Running to well over 150 pages plus diagrams and photographs, it is too vast a document even to summarise here, but some of its more interesting findings are worth looking at. Some are too obvious to raise an eyebrow, such as the fact that 50 per cent of the tanks knocked out were Shermans; although 16 per cent Comets, for their short time in service, against a mere 3 per cent Challengers does seem strange. Possibly it is a reflection of the unpopularity of the latter, suggesting that it simply was not being employed very vigorously, whereas the Comet, in which crews had greater confidence, was used more aggressively. As for means of destruction it is again no surprise to learn that 41 per cent were due to armour-piercing shot against 31 per cent for mines, but the compilers were surprised to record a figure of 22 per cent for hollow-charge weapons, most of which they believed to be of the Panzerfaust type. They contrasted this with a corresponding figure of 10 per cent for the period before the Rhine crossing. With hindsight we should not be so surprised. For one thing it would have been a lot more difficult to get close enough to a tank to guarantee a hit when it was bowling along a French highway at 30 mph than when stalking a more cautious one in the close, forested country of one's own homeland. The majority of hits against tanks were from the front, and on the turret. This is not so surprising in the case of heavy anti-tank weapons but it does seem a bit unusual when hand-held weapons are considered. For a start, one imagines that Panzerfaust-equipped infantry would have preferred to fire at a tank as it passed, rather than while it was still heading for them since, if they had missed, it could easily have opened fire or even given chase. Further, the fact that 50 per cent of Panzerfaust hits were on the turret, against some 30 per cent for all other armour-piercing weapons, strikes one as curious because it suggests that the weapon would have had to have been elevated, and thus was more exposed, in firing. However, the awkward, underarm stance adopted by the Panzerfaust firer no doubt accounts for this.

Another point worth noting is that the most prevalent conventional anti-tank weapon was the PAK 7.5-cm KwK40 gun, the weapon mounted in later versions of the Panzer IV as well as various self-propelled guns: so much for the theory favoured by many Allied survivors, armoured and infantry, that nearly every enemy tank they met was either a Tiger or Panther. On the other hand, when a tank was hit by an 88-mm projectile, the killing rate was much higher, well above that for the 75-mm, and nearly twice that of a Panzerfaust. The researchers discovered that the average range of engagement was 600 yards, but this figure was not calculated to include short-range hollow-charge weapons. What they did notice was that for both types of weapon the percentage of shots which actually penetrated was around 50 to 60 per cent. They also commented on multiple strikes, which were discovered on less than 50 per cent of wrecks examined; of these, almost all had been caused by anti-tank weapons firing at some range. In other words it was very rare to find a tank damaged by more than one shot from a hand-held weapon, for the very good reason that the Panzerfaust was

a one-shot weapon and once it had been fired the crew either fled from, or were attacked by, the tank's escorting infantry.

From the cold statistics of machinery the investigators moved on to the more emotive subject of human casualties. Overall, 38 per cent of these were fatal. Under attack from anti-tank or hollow-charge weapons, casualty figures conformed to the scale of hits recorded above; that is the majority (1.4 casualties per tank) were caused by armour-piercing shot. 1.3 by hollow charge, yet a mere 0.4 where tanks ran on to mines. This would appear to have been due to mines being detonated under tanks' tracks and not, normally, under the hull. The detailed breakdown of casualties, taken by type of tank involved, position of crewman or location of strike did not bring out any meaningful figures beyond the rather pointless one that Sherman Fireflys sustained a higher percentage of injuries per head of crew, simply because there was no hull machine-gunner, so the number of heads to spread it over was less. What was significant, although again the finding did not apply to any particular type of tank rather than any other, was that 25 per cent of all casualties were burns. Thus the Sherman's particular reputation as a so-called Tommy Cooker was undeserved as far as this survey was concerned. Gunners, apparently, got more severely burned more often than other crew members. One interesting point, which could not be fully confirmed through lack of data, was that casualties in Churchill, where they were examined, did not differ significantly, either in scale or type, from those in any other kind of tank.

The Allied armies that were now rolling through Germany had the scent of victory to savour. They had come a long way and had learnt a great deal in the process; they were professional, confident yet cautious. Time and trial had weeded out the worst of their equipment and they had also studied how to make the best use of what they did have. In some cases the results were surprising – for instance, some Daimler armoured cars had been shorn of

123   A Sherman V, penetrated and then blown apart by an internal explosion. An awful sight for a tank soldier.

124 *A White scout car at the garden gate, well cluttered up with home comforts. A good example of a generally useful armoured vehicle.*

125 *One of the massive AEC six-wheel drive armoured command vehicles, showing the limited visibility available from the driver's position.*

their turrets and turned into SODs, or Sawn-Off Daimlers, as a species of enlarged scout car for unit commanders. The same thing happened to at least one Staghound. The American-built half-tracks, which had first made a name for themselves in Italy, were now everywhere and fulfilling every role imaginable, but only rarely, at least in British service, as armoured personnel carriers, the task for which they had been designed. Observers of this cavalcade of armour would also have noticed considerable numbers of the venerable White Scout Cars still operational with the British forces, largely in the support role, never as scouts, but in one instance at least now in the very forefront of technology. This was for the purpose of sonic warfare, more correctly called sonic deception. These cars were equipped with huge loudspeakers and amplification equipment, the speakers being

mounted on hydraulic elevating apparatus. The idea was to have these cars stalk about the battlefield in certain chosen locations and play noisy recordings of battle, or the preparations for battle, to the attentive enemy. In theory, no unit would evacuate a defensive position to assist a more threatened zone if they were made to believe that an attack was imminent in their own area. Whether such a ruse was ever effective, or the sounds played were really convincing, is difficult to say, but the whole scheme was surrounded with such secrecy that more than forty years passed before much information emerged about it. White Scout Cars were also modified into compact, indeed cramped, command vehicles with hard-top roofs in British service, but at the same time something appeared at the other end of the scale.

This was the huge AEC Model 0857 Armoured Command Vehicle, a 19-ton, six-wheel drive giant, some 26 ft long and powered by a 150 bhp diesel engine. Construction began in 1944, but so far no conclusive photographic evidence has been found to prove that they saw active service before VE Day. They would certainly have proved a handful on the road, with the driver viewing the world from his elevated station through a narrow visor across a vast expanse of armoured bonnet. As with the earlier Matador-based type there were High Power and Low Power versions, denoting different combinations of radio set. The crew remained at eight, although they were more spaciously and comfortably accommodated.

In *The Great Tank Scandal*, reference was made to a report entitled *Weapons for the Army* compiled by the House of Commons Select Committee on National Expenditure, dated 26 August 1942. Although not expressly charged with continuing this investigation, the Committee deemed it their duty to observe and report on subsequent developments. From this they appear to have become sufficiently concerned for the chairman, Sir John Wardlaw-Milne MP, to address a further report to the Prime Minister under the title of a *Memorandum on Tank Production* dated 11 March 1944. On 29 May 1946 the honourable member for Ipswich, the indefatigable Richard Rapier Stokes again, asked in the House of Commons that both reports be made public and, in response, this was undertaken by the Lord President of the Council. The document, a fifty-eight-page booklet entitled *War-Time Tank Production*, was published by His Majesty's Stationery Office in July 1946; if anyone actually bought one it would have cost one shilling.

Some of the most significant pieces of evidence from this report have been drawn on already in this book, but at this point it is worth looking at a few of the more general points that it raised. In a way it is a pity that the Committee felt compelled to send their report to the Prime Minister as early as March. This meant that most of their evidence was drawn from the moribund year of 1943, yet it was too late for any drastic improvements to be implemented before the invasion of Europe. At the same time this enabled the Prime Minister, under the valid excuse of excessive pressure on the War Cabinet, to hold off from making a detailed reply until after the invasion. In fact he did not send it until 2 August 1944, by which time the success of British arms on the Continent entirely drew its sting, especially after Field Marshal Montgomery had said such nice things about the Cromwell, a tank which the Select Committee had particularly singled out for criticism.

They had reserved their harshest comments for the Ministry of Supply and had suggested that, in future, the War Office should take the lead in the provision of technical military equipment since, in theory, they had a better idea of what was wanted. They regarded the appointment of a Deputy Chief of the Imperial General Staff, with a seat on the War Council, as the officer responsible for weapon supply to the army as being a step in the right direction. They also noted the unfortunate position of the hapless Tank Board, remarking that it had drifted into the position of being a body for recording decisions reached at a lower level – little more than an ineffective rubber stamp. They felt it should be reduced in size, headed by a chairman who was a War Office representative and also demanded members on the War Office side with recent fighting experience.

Perhaps their most interesting and effective contribution, however, was reserved for the industrial side. Here they made a point that has been overlooked by most tank historians since then: the subject of corporate responsibility. Drawing a comparison with the Royal Air Force, they pointed out that every time a Lancaster bomber went into the air the reputation of the A V Roe Company, and by association that of the entire Hawker-Siddeley group,

went with it. The same was true of the Hurricane, or the Vickers-Supermarine Spitfire. Search through a catalogue of aircraft and you will find that in nearly every country the name or type number of any plane is inextricably united with that of its manufacturer, or at least the parent design company. Compare this with the tanks.

If the case is regarded from the press or public awareness level, then it is just possible that the Valentine was associated with Vickers-Armstrong, but how many people instinctively linked the name of Churchill with Vauxhall, or Crusader with Nuffield? And did anyone at all associate the Covenanter, for instance, with the name of the London, Midland and Scottish Railway Company? To be fair, as the Committee admitted, Vickers-Armstrong no doubt felt themselves responsible for the Valentine, and indeed Vauxhall Motors for the Churchill, but they added that this might have been why these were two of the more successful British tanks. But who staked their reputation on Cromwell – Rolls-Royce, Leylands, Metropolitan? The first might have had some justification if they had done more than initiate the design, but it was soon entirely out of their hands and, as far as the public was concerned, the various British cruiser tanks might just as well have sprung up out of the ground. It might seem a petty point, but in fact there is probably a great deal of validity in it. Look at armoured cars for instance: apart from the Coventry (which in any case had the reputation of a great industrial city in its care) and just possibly the Humber, which ought properly to have been called a Karrier, every British armoured car was known exclusively by its manufacturer's name. Indeed many of them made good capital out of it – by 1944, for instance, the Daimler Company was drawing on the reputation of its armoured cars to sell motor cars once wartime restrictions were lifted. Why one and not the other? It is impossible to say. Yet even today, despite the Select Committee's sound conclusion, no British AFV, not even an armoured car, employs its maker's name as part of its official title.

Nobody, except perhaps Mr Stokes, could call the Prime Minister's belated response a whitewash, but there was an element of all's well that ends well about it. Each point was dealt with and answered, if not comprehensively, at least with the directness one associates with Winston Churchill. In the end, perhaps, it was a question of standpoint. At the Select Committee's end of the telescope certain things loomed large and it was inevitable that many of their witnesses should have been people with a critical attitude; there was enough evidence if one asked for it. Conversely, from where the Prime Minister stood, things looked a lot better, at a distance. His advisors were there to place a positive interpretation on things, possibly for a variety of motives, and if they could produce convincing explanations then that must suffice. In this connection it is worth remarking that in the copy of the report which once belonged to the Director, Royal Armoured Corps, Major-General Raymond Briggs – now held in the Tank Museum

Library – the passages he had highlighted mostly concern Churchill's more effective ripostes.

The war in the West was almost over. The Soviet Red Army was forcing the gates of Berlin and, with mobility restored as resistance collapsed, the British armoured divisions were once again racing for their final objectives, the German ports on the North Sea Coast. And although the Select Committee may not have known it, Britain was on the verge of redeeming itself as an inspired, tank-designing nation; Montgomery's Universal Tank was on its way. Before rounding off this account with an examination of this excellent machine, mention should be made to three projects which were killed off at the design stage by Germany's unconditional surrender.

General Staff specification number A40 was allocated to a tank described as A30 Stage 2. This implies a Mark II version of the Challenger, and although no other details are available there is no good reason to link this with the other A30 design, otherwise SP2, the tank destroyer Avenger which was a Royal Artillery equipment. Just a few more details survive of A44, described as a development of the A34 Comet with a 57-inch turret ring, capable of mounting either the 6-pounder-, 75-mm or 95-mm weapons, with a weight of 30 tons. A design which sounds like a Comet with Cromwellian firepower – a singularly pointless exercise to all appearances, given that Cromwells lasted in service for just as long as Comets. Finally, even the mighty Tortoise was not to be spared. A Mark II is mentioned with a 1,000-hp engine, although what this might have been is not specified. Whether this was the same thing as Turtle, another Tortoise-like proposal, is also unclear. As explained in the introduction it was not the intention to cover the development of self-propelled artillery in this volume, but since one type does directly concern the Royal Armoured Corps, it should just be mentioned. The practice of including a heavy troop in armoured car regiments to provide fire support has been explained, including the fact that to be truly effective they had to be able to operate off the road. This need was met by the 75-mm gun American half-tracks, but a replacement for these was chosen in the form of a small, self-propelled version of the Harry Hopkins light tank, the 95-mm gun Alecto. In fact none were issued for service until after the war ended but one, and possibly two armoured car regiments operated a troop of these compact and highly mobile vehicles in the Middle East just after the war.

In a strictly literal sense the Universal Tank which has been the theme of this book was a myth, but in one sense, the sense that Montgomery meant with his Capital Tank, it already existed in the Sherman. However the title was selected as a pointer to the theory which lay behind the ultimate British tank of the Second World War, the Centurion. This can be detected in a quotation from the half-yearly Report of the Royal Armoured Corps issued at the end of December 1942: 'The appearance of the Sherman, and the trend towards a common tactical doctrine for tank and armoured brigades since the battle of El Alamein convinces the General Staff of the advantages of a universal tank.' It was required be within a 40-ton weight limit in order to match current military bridging and to mount a dual-purpose 75-mm gun, although a proportion should be fitted with a 17-pounder 'hole punching' weapon, while others carried multiple 20-mm guns for anti-aircraft work. The aim was to be standardisation, but not stagnation. As early as August 1942 the General Staff Committee had asked the Directorate of Armoured Fighting Vehicles to produce specifications for a 'general service' tank, with the following features listed in order of priority from the top: reliability, gun power, speed, radius of action, armour protection and finally a well-planned fighting compartment. This would seem to have been clear enough. The General Staff, taking heed of the situation, was formulating a long-term plan even while the short-term schemes already described were developing in their wayward fashion. But it was not as simple as that.

In October 1942 General A C Richardson, on behalf of the General Staff, had addressed a memorandum to the Tank Board, most of which consisted of sharp, if rather retrospective, criticism. Yet the last paragraph, a single sentence, suggested a whole new line of approach: 'Has not the state of the art on both sides of the Atlantic reached a stage when we should be well advised to harness the design resources of both countries to the development of a Victory Tank for common production?' Stung into an equally sharp reply, Commander Micklem, for the Tank Board, made some attempt to justify the unjustifiable, complained that there was little point in 'jobbing backwards' and suggested that if the General Staff really intended to have a go at the Tank Board they should come out and say so. Then he took a calculated swipe at Richardson:

> The suggestion contained in your last paragraph appears to be totally unrealistic. To assume that it is practicable to design a successful tank jointly between the USA and UK shows a complete failure to appreciate the problems involved in producing a successful design of tank. Further, the specification of the Victory Tank is not included in the memorandum, nor does it state the purpose for which such a tank is required.

Evidently Micklem did not know that in 1918 Britain and the United States had co-operated in the design of an excellent tank, the Mark VIII, and neither did Richardson. But what was the Victory Tank? Despite what Micklem said, its purpose must have been obvious from its title: he should have asked about its role. The chances are that it was an expression which Richardson simply plucked from the air, but in his reply to Micklem he enclosed the General Staff Statement of Policy on Tanks dated 10 September 1942. Based on the list of priorities already quoted, this called for a Medium Cruiser as the standard type of tank and a Heavy Tank which sacrificed gun power, number of crew, radius of action and speed in favour of armour. For a long-term project it recommended serious consideration of American designs such as the T20. None of this sounds very convincing and it is made even worse by a document with more or less the same title issued by the Tank Board in February 1943. This goes to great lengths, explaining what is actually going on and then turns to new projects, among which is an armoured aircraft, but nothing at all to meet the demand for a Universal or Victory tank, call it what you will.

The paper war between Richardson and Micklem was still going on in June 1943 but it had degenerated into recriminations and justifications for past events and paid very little attention to the future. In the mean time the General Staff had revised their policy on tanks in a paper with that title issued on 9 March 1943. This again listed the Medium Cruiser type but, instead of the proposed Heavy Tank, now substituted a Heavy Cruiser which appears to have been an optimum combination of armament and armour up to whatever reasonable limit a good power-to-weight ratio could be maintained, always given that reliability remained the absolute priority. In July 1943 the Deputy Chief of the Imperial General Staff, Sir Ronald Weeks, delivered a paper to the Secretary of State for War which, after expressing concern over the tank situation, closed by saying: 'The question of future tanks including a British TIGER is under consideration, but it will probably be 10 days before we can tackle this subject.' It is fruitless even to try and decide if the Universal tank, Heavy Cruiser, Victory Tank and British Tiger were all the same thing, although it seems reasonable to assume that they all expressed the same ideal in a rather vague way. Things came more sharply into focus in September when the Secretary of State received another note, this time from General Weeks's chief. This also rounded off with a glance into the future, backed up this time by reference to a recently compiled table which showed, on a year-by-year basis, the comparative increase in size and performance of German and British tank weapons, proving in fact that there was no comparison. It then went on to say that Britain should 'make a bold jump in an endeavour to outstrip German development. Hitherto we have been trying to catch up and have failed'. It then went on to advocate a new cruiser with 4 in. of frontal armour, mounting a 17-pounder or 3.7-in. gun, 'which is likely to be superior to any weapon which the enemy can mount in a tank'. The writer did not anticipate that such a design would be cleared, or production started, much before the beginning of 1945.

A matter of days after this document was completed the General Staff issued another Policy on Tanks paper which actually contained a reference to long-term policy. Anyone expecting a decisive lead from it would have been sorry to discover none. Indeed it was made clear that both infantry and cruiser tanks were required, even beyond the foreseeable future, but while some ideal specifications were given

for the former, nothing but the most general requirements were laid down for the cruiser. Such details were left to the Tank Board who, in November, made their first specific reference to the new tank. A meeting early in the month considered the latest General Staff specifications and, after fixing up details of A34 Comet production with representatives from Leyland Motors, went on to discuss a new tank under the designation A41. It may well be that the reluctance, shown earlier by Leyland, to get involved with Comet, was the result of a desire to take charge of this new product, but if so they were to be disappointed. The Tank Board took note of a Ministry of Supply recommendation that design and production of prototypes should be carried out independently of Leyland Motors, the aim being to have pilots and pre-production models ready towards the end of 1944, with production getting started on a small scale by the second quarter of 1945. Initial specifications called for a tank weighing up to 45 tons, with 4 in. of frontal armour, powered by a Meteor engine with Merrit-Brown transmission and turret ring diameter certainly no less than that of the Sherman. The armament was to be a 17-pounder, with coaxial machine-gun, with a later option on a 37-pounder weapon firing separated ammunition, but a strong hint was given that no hull machine-gun was required. This was said to offer considerable advantages in the design of the front end and driver's compartment, in addition to providing extra space for ammunition stowage.

With Leylands out of the picture, development of the new tank was handed over entirely to the Department of Tank Design. This was the first such project that they would be responsible for since the war began, and bearing in mind the result it is, perhaps, a pity that they had not been employed to do what their title suggests a good deal earlier. By the end of December 1943 a full-size mock-up was under construction at the AEC works at Southall, west of London, and when this was completed, in May 1944, it was viewed by the Director, Royal Armoured Corps and members of the Tank Board. This meeting led to further discussions on armament, of the type that had confused all matters concerning British tank design for the last two years. The 17-pounder, it was accepted, was the best armour-piercing weapon currently available, while the 95-mm howitzer was equally ideal for firing high-explosive rounds. Neither of these guns pleased the dual-purpose weapon school, who pointed to the 77-mm as the most effective all-round gun, so the inevitable compromise was agreed. The first fifteen of the twenty pilot models should carry the 17-pounder, with a 77-mm gun in each of the remaining five. A 95-mm gun version might come later. As if this were not enough, arguments then broke out over the secondary weapon, between those who favoured an ordinary machine-gun and the more avant-garde element who believed in a heavier, 20-mm, automatic weapon, this last was being strongly promoted by Major-General Sir Campbell Clarke, the Director General of Artillery. Clarke was a great believer in the high-velocity gun in a tank, on the grounds that its primary task was the destruction of other tanks. Those who favoured a dual-purpose weapon did so because they felt it was more useful for dealing with anti-tank guns and other soft targets. Clarke argued that in such a case the 20-mm Polsten cannon was a better bet. It could defeat any unarmoured target and pierce the shields of anti-tank guns, providing the best of both worlds. Whichever main gun was mounted, there was still a large faction in favour of the ordinary, rifle-calibre machine-gun because it was capable of sustained fire and its large store of ammunition took up less room inside the tank. The Polsten had a bulky, thirty-round magazine which was difficult to change quickly, so that sustained fire was not possible. Indeed the pro-machine-gun lobby was so influential that at one stage there was talk of fitting a pair of coaxial Besas alongside the main gun and another in the rear of the turret. This last was connected with the use of the 17-pounder. In the A41, as designed, the main armament protruded well ahead of the hull so there would be many occasions when it would be safer for the tank to proceed with the turret reversed. Under such circumstances a Besa at the back of the turret would be pointing forwards, ready for action in an emergency. In the end it was agreed that of the 17-pounder pilots, the first five would feature a coaxial Besa while the remaining ten would have the Polsten, or a Besa, in an independent mounting to the left of the main armament. The rear-mounted machine-gun was rejected when the designers pointed out that once fitted where would be no room for the internal 2-in. smoke bomb discharger, and this last being a General Staff specification where the rear Besa was not, then the Besa had to go. Some, the DRAC amongst them, still hankered after a hull machine-gun as well, but this was finally rejected following trials in an experimental hull, for a variety of reasons. In the first place such a mounting compromised the integrity of the sloping front hull plate, and it could only be fitted at the expense of ten rounds of ammunition. Furthermore, since no co-driver was contemplated, it was considered difficult for the driver to reload or clear stoppages while trying to drive at the same time.

Another DRAC recommendation that was taken up concerned the demand for an all-round vision cupola, although it was clear that this could not be incorporated without a complete redesign of the turret. Since this coincided with plans to improve the new tank's armour protection, it went ahead under the designation A41A. This version featured a cast turret with a plate roof welded in place, in the same way as that evolved for the A22F, heavy Churchill.

The new tank was christened Centurion, and even a quick look would convince anyone that it was a vast improvement over any of the cruiser tanks that had gone before. It was bigger, for a start, with a well-sloped glacis plate and boat-shaped hull to deflect mine blast. Christie

suspension was finally abandoned because it was estimated that it could not support such a heavy tank and still leave a generous margin of safety for improvements. Instead a new system was developed, on the Horstmann principle, by AEC and their designer G J Rackham who, as a young Tank Corps Lieutenant, had been involved in tank design in the First World War. This in turn meant that the hull sides were only of single thickness plates, unlike the Cromwell, for instance, which made it easier to keep the new tank narrow enough to cross existing Bailey bridges. On the other hand the advent of man-portable, hollow charge anti-tank weapons required a return to that other popular feature of the early war years, side-skirting plates covering the suspension. Centurion was undoubtedly a man's tank. Wartime experience with Crusader finished off any affection there might have been for mechanically assisted controls, so driving came down to a matter of main strength. A gear change which might have been easy on a 28 ton, 20-ft long Cromwell, became quite a challenge on Centurion which weighted 43 tons and was nearly 25-ft long. Changing gear was a two-handed job, and getting down from second gear to first quite a struggle at any time. Even so, a manual gearbox was not all that was on offer. The sibilant Sinclair-Meadows Synchro Self-Shifting Powerflow transmission was also investigated and installed in the enlarged A41S hull later in the year, although it was regarded as insufficiently developed at the time and was not proceeded with. Initial production was undertaken by the Royal Ordnance Factories, at Woolwich and Nottingham. By April 1945 three prototypes were at the Fighting Vehicle Proving Establishment, Chertsey, another was at Lulworth for gunnery trials and two more were on the point of delivery. It was therefore agreed that the best possible trial these early models could receive was ordeal by battle, and a scheme was initiated to rush them out to Germany.

Under the codename Operation Sentry the intention was to attach the six tanks to the Guards Armoured Division which would evaluate them under combat conditions. Crews were drawn from the Grenadier, Coldstream, Irish and Welsh Guards under the command of

126 *A Centurion Mark I, Sheila,* which took part in Operation Sentry. *The turret is reversed and the 20-mm Polsten visible in its separate mounting.*

Captain Sir Martin Beckett MC of the Welsh Guards. Before preliminary training could start, however, Germany surrendered, and it was announced that among the regiments destined to lose their tanks almost at once were all those that formed the Guards Armoured Division. The trial would go ahead, but the tank crews would now form the Guards Detachment which, for administrative purposes, would attach itself to 7th Armoured Division. The tanks left Southampton in landing craft on 14 May 1945 and landed at Antwerp five days later. From here they commenced a long road march of over 400 miles across Belgium and Holland to join up with 7th Armoured Division headquarters at Gribbohm in Germany, close to the Kiel Canal. This marked the start of a round of road and cross-country trials which included a competitive swamp-crossing test in the presence of the sinister-sounding Mud Committee, in which the Centurion was soundly beaten by a Cromwell and Chaffee. Gunnery trials were carried out and every opportunity taken for familiarisation visits to other armoured regiments in Germany before the tanks returned home, via Calais, at the end of July.

Favourable opinion was unanimous. Most crews who tried the tanks, even for a few days, declared them to be the best they had ever seen, although nobody had anything very good to say about the Polsten cannon. Many small, but constructive criticisms were offered and the most obvious weakness shown up by the trials involved the front idler bracket, a continuing source of trouble in British-designed tanks, which tended to shear off under stress. Compared with what they had been used to, it was only right that British tank crews should have allowed themselves to get a bit carried away by Centurion. Yet it is only fair to balance this by pointing out that in most respects the new tank was no more than the equal of a German Panther, and that tank dated from 1943.

It seems almost perverse to begin a story at the end of a book, but the saga of the Centurion is a long one. Forty-five years after the events just recounted, some Centurions accompanied the British Army to war once again, in the Persian Gulf, and it seems quite safe to prophesy that some will remain in service somewhere when their fiftieth anniversary comes around. What this means, of course, is that here at last the British Army was in possession of a British-designed and British-built tank which, taken all round, was probably superior to any tank in the world. Not only that, but the basic design was so good that it proved possible to uparmour and upgun the Centurion more than once in its service career and to adapt it to many other ancillary roles without ever compromising its qualities.

But was Centurion, after all, the Universal Tank? The answer has to be a qualified negative. That title was given to the contemporary A45 at one point, but A45 never got beyond the development stage, although it contributed to the design of the heavy gun tank Conqueror. And when Conqueror bowed out in 1966, the FV4201 Chieftain was just entering service. As the first Main Battle Tank, Chieftain was probably better qualified for the title, but it was a world away from the Cromwells and Churchills of 1944. If one regards Conqueror as an aberration, then it does seem reasonable to claim that Centurion embodied all the wartime ideals of what the universal tank should be, and in that sense alone it justifies the title. Looking back over the war years there can be no room for complacency. On the design and production side, much of what occurred was little short of a scandal, and even allowing for the initial reverse occasioned by Dunkirk, it is difficult to find enough convincing excuses to explain everything. If matters were redeemed by more than the Sherman then it was by Robert Crisp, and the many tank men like him, who knew the odds and did not flinch, even when it meant stalking a tank of twice the size and power in order to ensure victory. There is poetic justice in the ultimate appearance of the superb Centurion, and classic irony in the fact that it arrived in Germany just too late.

The atom bomb did more than end the Second World War with a bang. To some minds it rendered the tank and all conventional weapons to the scrap-heap under the option of total oblivion. Yet it is not the human way to take the long view and then sit back, waiting for it to happen. As in 1918, military technology was attaining new peaks just as the major conflict ended in 1945 and, despite peacetime economies, it continued to thrive. If armoured vehicles could not be produced for war, they could always be manufactured for export, and now there was not a country in the world which considered itself worthy of the name if it did not own some armoured cars or tanks. Thus, at least the tank became universal, even if there never was such a thing as a Universal Tank.

Index

Aberdeen Proving Ground 86
Adder 64
AEC Ltd. 50, 93, 120
AFVs, Australian
 Armoured Command Vehicle 67
 Australian Cruiser 65, 66
 Dingo 66
 Rhino 67
 Rover 66, 67
AFVs, British
 A10 111
 A12 Matilda 15, 16, 31, 33, 50, 55,
  64–67
 A13 Covenanter 33, 43, 46, 54, 70, 118
 A15 Crusader 3, 9, 11, 15, 19, 21,
  33–36, 40, 43, 69, 73, 118, 121
 A17 Tetrarch 42, 43, 71, 98
 A22 Churchill 12, 17–19, 25–29, 31,
  33, 35, 37, 40, 44–49, 52–55, 63, 70,
  79, 82, 85–88, 92, 94, 98–100, 104,
  106, 108, 114–118, 121
 A24 Cavalier 33, 35, 36, 68
 A25 Harry Hopkins 42, 101, 119
 A27L Centaur 36, 68, 81, 86, 90, 96–
  98, 106–108, 110
 A27M Cromwell 17, 34–36, 38, 43, 56,
  58, 68, 70, 80–86, 90–92, 95, 98,
  100, 111–114, 118–122
 A30 Avenger 119
 A30 Challenger 34, 83–85, 101, 112,
  116, 119
 A33 Excelsior 86, 114
 A34 Comet 65, 82, 103, 112–120
 A38 Valiant 87–89
 A39 Tortoise 89–92, 115, 119
 A41 Centurion 65, 82, 112, 114, 119–
  122
 A43 Black Prince 114, 115
 AEC Armoured Car 6, 16, 19, 40, 73,
  101
 AEC Armoured Command Vehicle
  4×4 67
 AEC Armoured Command Vehicle
  6×6 117
 Alecto 42, 101, 119
 Archer 44
 Coventry Armoured Car 4, 10, 118
 Crossley Armoured Car 61
 Daimler Armoured Car 4, 13, 20, 40,
  117
 Daimler Scout Car 4, 9, 19, 21, 75, 102
 FV214 Conqueror 122
 FV601 Saladin 73
 FV4201 Chieftain 122
 Humber Armoured Car 4, 20, 40, 78,
  95
 Humber Light Recce Car 9, 59

 Humber Scout Car 41, 42, 102
 Light Tank Mark II 61
 Light Tank Mark VI 59, 61, 62
 Loyd Carrier 24, 77
 Morris Light Recce Car 9
 Nellie 35, 89
 TOG 38, 83, 86, 89, 112
 Universal Carrier 22–24, 47, 55, 57,
  59, 74, 77, 79, 94, 98
 Valentine 4, 9–11, 16–19, 27, 31, 39,
  43, 50, 54, 56, 60, 63, 67, 107
 Vampire 43
 Vanguard 43, 44
AFVs, Canada
 C15T 79
 Caplad 79
 Fox 78, 79
 Grizzly 77
 Lynx 61, 62, 78
 Otter 79
 Ram 18, 46, 77, 80, 106
 Sexton 106
 Snowmobile 79
 Tracked Jeep 79
 Windsor 77
AFVs German
 Panzer III 11, 12
 Panzer IV 11, 12, 84, 99, 111, 116
 Panzer V Panther 27, 85, 91, 92, 99,
  111–114, 116, 122
 Panzer VI Tiger 11–13, 72, 82–85,
  99, 111, 114, 116
 Panzer VI Tiger II 73, 111
AFVs India
 Carrier Indian Pattern 58–61, 67, 79
AFVs South Africa
 Marmon-Herrington Armoured
  Cars 7, 8, 59
AFVs United States
 Half-Tracks 19, 73, 75, 101, 117
 Landing Vehicle, Tracked 32, 75, 106,
  109
 M3 Grant 3, 11, 14, 17, 55, 59–66, 95,
  102
 M3 Lee 17, 55, 59–64, 71, 76
 M3 Stuart 3, 6, 14, 21, 58–64, 67, 101
 M4 Sherman series 3, 11, 13–19, 25–
  32, 38, 46–51, 54–57, 60–64, 68–72,
  76, 80, 85, 91–96, 98, 100–108,
  112–116, 119–122
 M5 Stuart 67, 71, 115
 M6 Staghound 19, 31, 73, 95, 117
 M6 Tank 72
 M8 Greyhound 21, 74
 M10 Tank Destroyer 29, 31, 98
 M22 Locust 71, 72, 115
 M24 Chaffee 71, 101

 M26 Pershing 65, 73
 M38 Armoured Car 73
 T1 Tank 87
 T14 Tank 72, 86
 T16 Carrier 74, 77, 107
 T18 Boarhound 8, 73
 T19 Armoured Car 73
 T20 Tank 72, 120
 T23 Tank 72, 102
 White Scout Car 4, 5, 19, 75, 78, 117
AFVs USSR
 T-34 Tank 91
Ainsworth, Harry 34
Aldershot 34, 45
Allen Muntz Bat 42
American Locomotive Co. 86
Amphibious Training & Development
 Centre 64
AMRA/AMRCA 16, 48, 80
Anti-Tank Experimental
 Establishment 45
Anzio 25
Arakan 60
Ardeer Aggie 108
ARK 30, 52, 63, 105–108
Ark Royal HMS 30
Armoured Force Board 72
Armoured Trailer Nº 1 92
Army, British;
 21st Army Group 98, 99
 2nd Army 96
 8th Army 8–11, 13, 38, 40
 14th Army 61
 Divisions
 1st Armoured Division 3, 8
 6th Armoured Division 10, 11, 13, 19
 7th Armoured Division 3, 100
 10th Armoured Division 69
 11th Armoured Division 11
 79th Armoured Division 45, 49, 52,
  55, 94, 96, 105–107
 Guards Armoured Division 121
 6th Airborne Division 98, 115
 Brigades
 2nd Armoured Brigade 3
 4th Armoured Brigade 102
 7th Armoured Brigade 58
 8th Armoured Brigade 3
 22nd Armoured Brigade 2
 23rd Armoured Brigade 10, 18
 26th Armoured Brigade 11
 29th Armoured Brigade 103, 113
 34th Armoured Brigade 101
 21st Army Tank Brigade 12, 13, 18
 25th Army Tank Brigade 12, 13, 18
 Regiments (RAC)
 3rd Carabiniers 62

2nd Dragoons (Greys) 14
3rd King's Own Hussars 59
4th Queen's Own Hussars 32
7th Queen's Own Hussars 58
8th King's Royal Irish Hussars 101
10th Prince of Wales Own Hussars 32
11th Prince Albert's Own Hussars 4, 5, 13
16th/5th Lancers 10, 11
17th/21st Lancers 9, 10
25th Dragoons 61
26th Hussars 58, 61
2nd Royal Tank Regiment 32, 58
3rd Royal Tank Regiment 14
12th Royal Tank Regiment 12
48th Royal Tank Regiment 12
51st Royal Tank Regiment 12
North Irish Horse 12
1st Derbyshire Yeomanry 9
2nd Derbyshire Yeomanry 21
Westminster Dragoons 81
2nd Lothian & Border Horse 10
3rd/4th County of London
    Yeomanry 100, 101
116 RAC 60
142 RAC 12
145 RAC 11
146 RAC 60
149 RAC 61
150 RAC 61
152 RAC 55
158 RAC 61
159 RAC 61
160 RAC 61
163 RAC 61
6th Airborne Recce Regiment 98
56th Reconnaissance Regiment 9
Nº1 Scorpion Regiment 15, 28
other regiments
Argyll & Sutherland Highlanders 59
Queen's Regiment 32
Royal Air Force Regiment 9
Royal Marines Assault Regiment
    96–98, 109
34 Amphibian Support Regiment
    RM 109
other units
29th Infantry Battalion RM 109
100 Independent Light Tank
    Squadron 59
400 Independent Scorpion
    Squadron 16, 28
401 Independent Scorpion
    Squadron 16, 28, 63
18 Base Workshops REME 25
Army, Canadian;
    1st Army 96
    4th Division 80
    1st ME Company 46
Army, German
    Afrika Korps 6, 8, 12
    21st Panzer Division 98
    501 Heavy Tank Battalion 12
    504 Heavy Tank Battalion 12
Army, Indian;
    3rd Cavalry Regiment 59
    7th Light Cavalry Regiment 63

Army, New Zealand;
    Corps 8
Army, United States;
    5th Army 21
    102nd Cavalry Reconnaissance
        Squadron 98
Assault Training & Development
    Centre 108
Aunt Jemima 93
Austin Motor Co. 90
Autocar Co. 75
AVRE 45–49, 53, 79, 94, 97, 105, 108, 109

Babcock & Wilcox 44
Badger 80
Badoglio, Marshal 19
Bantu 95
Baron 16, 50, 51
Bazooka 27
Beaulieu 57
Beaverbrook, Lord 34
Beckett MC, Capt. Sir Martin 122
Belch 56
Berkely Miller, Capt. J N 69
Birmingham Railway Carriage & Wagon
    Co. 33, 35, 82, 86, 90
Blackburn VC, Brigadier A S 59
Blacker, Colonel 46, 108
Blacker Developments Ltd. 46
Blackforce 59
Blade Force 9
Blagden, Col. W M 34
Bobbin 48, 105, 107
Borneo 64, 66
Bouchier, Col. A 69
Bougainville 64
Bovington 81
Bridgelayers 31, 43, 54, 63
Briggs, Gen. Raymond 69, 85, 100, 111, 118
Brighty, Maj. G 85
British Tank Mission 68, 74, 75, 86
Broom & Wade Ltd. 12
Brown, Capt. R B 14, 15
Bulldozer 32
Bullshorn 49, 105
Burmark 63
Burney, Sir Denistoun 108
Burton, Sir Geoffrey 33

Cadillac Co. 71
Canal Defence Light 53, 63, 75, 107
Carrier Wing 42
Carrot 46
Cassino 26, 28
Caterpillar D7 105
Centipede 107
Chevrolet 73
Chiang Kai-shek 103
Chindwin 58
Christchurch 52–54
Churchill, Winston 82, 89, 118, 119
CIRD 80, 94, 107
Clan Foundry 33
Clarke, Maj-Gen. Sir Campbell 39, 82, 120, 121

Clifford, Maj. 81
Cobra 64
Cocksedge & Co. 46
Combined Operations Executive 47
Conger 94, 107
COXE 109
Crisp MC. Maj. R J 111, 112, 122
Crocodile 54, 64, 105–107
Culin, Sgt. C G 98, 99
'Cygnet' Op. 32

DD Tank 32, 56, 61, 63, 75, 83, 104, 106
D-Day 55, 70, 75, 92, 96, 105–107
Denovan, Lt. J J 45, 46, 108
Department of Tank Design 17, 33, 45, 61, 114, 120
Detroit 68–70, 104
Dewar, Michael 68, 69, 75, 77
Diamond T Co. 75
Dieppe 8, 12, 46, 47
Directorate of AFVs 119
Donbiak 60, 61
Douglas Skymaster 71
'Dracula' Op. 81
Dragonfly 57
DUKW 106
Duncan, Sir Andrew 68, 82

Eisenhower, Gen. D D 8, 76, 102
Enfidaville 13
English Electric Co. 86, 87
English Steel Co. 80
Ernest Wright Ltd. 92
Experimental Bridging Establishment 52, 54

Falaise Gap 99
Farmer Deck 48
Farmer Front 48
Farnborough 34–36, 84
Fighting Vehicle Proving
    Establishment 43, 69, 74, 88, 90, 99, 106, 121
Fondouk Pass 11
Food Machinery Corp. 76
Ford Motor Co. 68, 74, 77, 78
Fort Knox 84
Fraser, R P 55
Frazer-Nash Ltd. 73
Freyberg VC, Gen. Sir Bernard 8
Frog 66

Galpin, Col. S G 52, 63
Gatehouse, Gen. Alec 69
Gazala 83
General Electric Co. 72
General Motors Co. 73, 78
Gibb, Claude 85
Gin-and-It 107
Global Tank Review 103
Goat 47
Gordon-Hall, Col. F W S 18, 24, 25, 91, 92, 99
Gothic Line 28
Great Eastern 108
Green, Col. G 69
Gregory, Capt. R E 14, 15

Grigg, Sir James 82
Guadalcanal 67
Gunnery School 13

Halifax bomber 98
Hamilcar glider 42, 72, 98, 115
Hamman Lif 13
Hammersley MP, Maj. 55, 82
Hankley Common 46
Harkness RAMC, Capt. 115
Harriman, Averell 69
Hawick 13
Hedgehog 66
Hermion SS 59
Hitler, Adolf 34
Hives, Lord 33, 34
Hobart, Maj-Gen P C S 12, 45
Holy Roller 107
Hopkins, Harry 42
Hopper 107
Hotchkiss et Cie 34
'Husky' Op. 28

International Harvester Co. 75

Java 59
Jeep 4
Jefferis, Maj. M R 49, 108
Jones, T C Ltd. 50, 53, 98

Kangaroo 32, 80, 106
Karrier Motors 41, 118
Kasserine Pass 11
Kid 47
King George VI 97

Lagonda 55, 64
Lakeman, Maj. Tom 53
Leese, Gen. Sir Oliver 12
Leyland Motors 33–36, 90, 112, 113, 118, 120
Littlejohn Adaptor 72
London, Midland & Scottish Railway 87, 118
Lucas Mission 69
Lucas, Oliver 34, 69
Lulu 95
Lulworth 13, 17, 34, 38, 40, 81, 84, 114, 115, 121
Macleod Ross, Brig. 69
Mareth Line 5, 8
Marmon-Herrington Co. 71, 79
Marquis 51, 93
Mechanisation Experimental Establishment 78, 79
Medenine 8
Melbourne 64
Messe, General 8
Metro-Cammell 42, 118
MG Car Co. 46, 53, 107
Micklem, Commander 82, 119, 120
Montgomery, Gen. B 8, 12–15, 19, 97, 99–103, 111, 118, 119
Montreal Locomotive Works 77

Morrell, Capt, P 25
Moses 107
Moyses, Harry 35
Mud Crossing Committee 107, 122
Mussolini, Benito 19

New Forest 57
New Guinea 64
Norman, Gen. Charles 10
Nuffield, Lord 36, 68, 80
Nuffield Mechanisation & Aero 33–37, 68, 69, 90
Obstacle Assault Centre 45, 48, 80
Octopus 29, 30, 51
Onion 47
Ordnance Board 70, 72, 73
O'Rorke, Lt-Col F D W 114, 115

Paget, Gen. Sir Bernard 92, 99
Panzerfaust 27, 104, 116
Penang 50
Percival, General 59
Petroleum Warfare Department 54
PIAT 24, 27
Pochin, Dr. 17
Porcupine 16
Pram Scorpion 50, 51
Pratt, Maj-Gen Douglas 69
Prong 98
Puckapunyal 65

Quinson Device 47

Rackham G J 121
Ramree Island 61
Rangoon 58, 63
Ransomes, Simms & Jefferies 48, 49
Rascal 109
Reo Motors 41
Rhine River 72, 104, 106, 113, 116
Richardson, Maj-Gen Alex 69–73, 119, 120
Roberts, Col. 'Pip' 12
Robotham, W A 33–35, 68, 70, 83, 84, 113
Roebling, Donald 75
Rolls-Royce Ltd. 33–35, 70, 83, 86, 90, 113, 118
Rommell, Gen. Erwin 8, 12
Ronald, Maj. K M 81
Ronson 57, 80
Roosevelt, President 42, 69
Rootes Group 40
Rootes, Sir William 68
Rotatrailer 92, 112
Royal Arsenal 38
Royal Ordnance Factory 85, 103, 121
Runstedt Field-Marshal von 111
Ruston & Hornsby Ltd 35, 88

Salamander 64
Samuel Butler Ltd. 48, 50
Sandys, Duncan 82, 89
'Savvy' Ex. 97

School of Infantry 85
School of Tank Technology 88, 112, 114
Senior Equitine Cultivator 49
'Sentry', Op. 121
Shattock, Capt. R G 14, 15
Singapore 59
Sitwell, Gen. 59
Slim, Gen. Sir William 64
Small Box Girder Bridge 53
Snake 16, 49
Somervell, Gen. 69, 70
Southend 61
Special Vehicle Development Committee 33
Spurrier, Henry 33
Steamroller Farm 13
Stern, Sir Albert 33
Stilwell, Gen. J 103
Stokes MP, Richard 82, 111, 112, 118
Stothert & Pitt 82–84
Straussler, Nicholas 57, 107
Sumatra 59

Tank Automotive Center 70
Tank Board 33–36, 38, 43, 69, 84, 89, 112, 119, 120
Tank Engine Mission 68
Tank Museum 118
Tarrant Rushton 98
Tapeworm 107
Terrapin 106
Thomas, Sir Miles 36, 68, 69, 89, 90
Toit, Maj. A du 50
'Torch' Op. 8, 9
'Totalize' Op. 106
'Trent' Ex. 13
Tugboat 107
'Turret' Op. 61
Typhoon fighter 113, 114

Vauxhall Motors 12, 33, 38, 44, 45, 75, 86, 87, 114, 118
Venning, Sir Walter 68
'Veritable' Op. 115
Verney, Maj-Gen. Gerald 100
Vickers-Armstrong 39, 42, 43, 74, 90, 112, 114, 118

Washington 68–70, 75, 92, 103
Wasp 55, 56, 80, 110
Wardlaw-Milne MP, Sir John 118
Weasel M29 106, 107
Weeks, Gen. Sir Ronald 39, 82, 92, 101, 102, 120
Wewak 64
White Motor Co. 75
'Whitehot' 25
Willys-Overland Co. 79
Witheridge, Col. George 84, 85
Worthington, Gen. 80
Wright RAMC, Capt. 115
Wurlitzer 94